The Ramblings of
Joseph Miller

by
Simon R. Brickell

Published 2003 by
Simon R. Brickell
20 Hobart Road
New Milton
Hants
BH25 6EG
England.
UK

Telephone 01425 616294

ISBN 0 954644 10 7

Printed by Creeds the Printers, Broadoak, Bridport DT6 5NL

To Ellie and Jack,
who stopped off at this world
to help me explore its many wonders

Chapter One

The moss on the arm of my garden seat reminded me of some distant valley that I must have seen either in my dreams or on television for I knew I'd never been there. Maybe the hypnotic flow of memory was confusing my sense of reality and perspective, but I was happy to swim along with it for the time being. If I'm honest, I only found myself in this state since I discovered the old seat ten minutes ago, when I noticed an old drawing pin that had once help hold up some balloons or ribbon or something, reflecting the sunlight like a tiny mirror in a confused sea of brambles, weeds and other now overgrown shrubbery. Of course with memories come emotions though quite what I was feeling I wasn't sure, all I did know was that I felt something other than a specific emotion, more of a muddled thought pattern, a bit, I suppose, similar to an adolescent attempt at asking a girl out, trying to control your body and mind but going through the exercise in a numb, trance-like effort.

As I looked around me various items caught my eye and thus triggered responses in me, some minor, others more of a general blanket emotion. The rope swing with the rough wooden seat that I tied up during some happy springtime, the bird box that I watched a pair of Bluetits raise a family, the rusty bolt on the back gate that despite my efforts to correct always dropped and became hard to close, the corner down at the end of the hedge where I used to sit surrounded by leaves and tree branches and imagine I was sat in the middle of a huge wood that no-one knew about, the old galvanised tub that I filled with water and laid half a breeze block and bricks in to help accommodate a couple of local frogs, and other things that I knew I had taken in subconsciously but didn't trigger in me, perhaps the most noticeable but for the wrong reasons. The moss on the arm next to me reminded me I was sitting on a rather dubious and damp piece of furniture so to save myself a possible unwanted encounter with a large clump of stinging nettles I rose and meandered along the cluttered pathways that now presented themselves. I was softly aware of various scents and aromas gently enticing the gaze of an eye which again began opening boxes of past times and events. An unexpected chuckle broke free as I walked past the old yet graceful apple tree or, to be more precise, the old 'hugging' tree. How many times had I thought this place to be too small and cramp, and yet now, even more crowded, it seemed to be infinitely full of events and outcomes.

As my eye was guided through the scene around me, like some elaborate and clever painting where the perspective and subject matter take you by the hand, I resisted going past, and paused at the top of a very sad looking stretch of ship lack fencing or rather the area of sky just above, where the early morning cumulus clouds were now casting off their veil of disguise and proudly shaping their form, like some exotic bird marking its territory to a possible onlooker. Reading their message but not for the moment cautious of it, I took time to study their form, their forces and their fading colours, trying to understand if they realised that they too were a result of a combining of circumstances and events. Strangely I felt a mutual respect between us, as if acknowledging that each were there in the present and by mere coincidence rather than causing the other to be there.

After awkwardly bidding them farewell I left the sky to evolve its destined form and was readjusting my focus to a nearer plane of sight when an intense patch of pure white snowdrops, gracefully arranged in a fairy ring, caused more homely emotions. I don't remember if we ever did tell our children the grown up truth, but certainly we made an effort at the time to allow them a child's fantasy by making out the fairies had planted them.

Now grown up, I suspect they knew that we had secretly planted them in a deliberate circle, indeed I suspect, they have already hatched the deception with their own children. I hope so.

Feeling a bit self conscious next to the open hedge that shielded the road from the contented interior, I made a deliberate effort to blend in more with the dense growth, away from possible enquiries and awkward questions. I had planned to see if the vegetable plot was still there, but after tripping, or rather being tripped, by a pugnacious shoot of a blackberry bush, I found myself both cursing and curious about an odd shaped ornament that like me was now laid on its side. We gazed at each other like a couple of young lovers laying in a field of corn, each about to offer their most precious emotions for the first time, but, through a fear of rejection, coldly agreeing that this was an alien position for the both of them. At least that's what I told myself the figure was thinking, and backed away from it and clumsily created the idea that I had something more important to do. I didn't remember buying the said item or accepting it as a gift, so without any feeling of guilt I left it there lying in its immobilised state with an empty beer can for company. Maybe inanimate objects could communicate with each other in some as yet undiscovered way. Perhaps right now they were both sharing a great sense of relief at being left alone in their secret world, joyful at the sense of continuance of their shared lifestyle. Grateful that the; in their minds, intruders threat had passed and that now reminded of their fortunate closeness can reaffirm their commitment to their cause by emitting their forces and creating a new mutant form of invisible molecular structure. Maybe they would be the Adam and Eve of a whole new creation of, to us humans, invisible and unheard civilisation. Maybe already, that deep in the now buried landfill sites of the country, a whole empire of major cities of these beings was thriving with no worries about NHS waiting lists, no bickering over a preferred inner city transport system, and who knows even a successful cricket team, well maybe they had a different name for it!

It always amazes me how when you tend a lawn the edges are forever encroaching into the borders, yet look at any overgrown plot and somehow, though the grass is anything up to three feet high, it seems to have lost most of its yearning to spread its feet and stray too far from its original placement. Funny that.

Walking sideways in some kind of confused Latin American dance routine, I tentatively deviated from the broken brick path and disturbed another disappointing realisation, like the time when you go back to or drive past your old school playing field or playground. What was once a never ending vista of pitches, hedges and tarmac, now seem little more than someone's back yard and garden. What was once the place you fired missiles from a new birthday present or played rebound with an endless number of angles to outsmart your mates, or the place where you once dropped the school tortoise after it started to pooh on your hand, all these things and many many more childhood dimensions are but a plot ready to be exploited by some greedy developer or now used as gardens for some attempt at converted flats. What had caused this comparison of dimensions was the now tiny battered wooden shed that had started life with great expectations. Here would be the place that would see the development of an invention, would proudly show off row upon row of gleaming tools, would be the perfect environment for selection and cultivation of various vegetables and annual bedding plants, a place to enjoy the smells of new wood, composts, oilstone and linseed, a place to be content while the visit lasted. Now what only just stood before me was a sad and decrepit old shell, where spiders had long since claimed squatters rights, and where the annual reunion of regional slugs was warmly entertained. No sign of mice or rats though, perhaps they could already see the decline in progress and didn't share the spiders and slugs opinion of a 'des res'. The little ledge where I used to put my tea mug reminded me that the sun had begun its daily arc through the sky and that by now I would have normally been completing a simple yet wholesome breakfast. I didn't feel hungry today, my body on some sort of standby was using a kind of adrenaline and defensive body reserves, a kind of high octane muesli overriding any pangs of hunger.

Saddened by the realisation of the sheds unhappy demise a fragrance teased my senses and offered a helping hand to guide to more happier things. Its source was not some sort of boy scout Jean Paul Gautier but a very gentle old friend, namely a sweet smelling Daphne. We had befriended each other some years ago whilst visiting relatives and on leaving their garden were formally introduced to each other. After exchanging polite curtesies the mother plant allowed me to take a cutting and the then young friend began residing in our garden. Strange how we have close friends whilst growing up, and then with a seamless joining of adulthood, we create new bonds and almost completely forget old allies until a piece of news or a historical reference is made and we become aware, for a short time, of things and people now filed away in the vaults of memory. Cuttings came to me, not railway or newspaper, though I confidently suspect they each could easily spend a while teasing further reminiscences with me, but the kind that nature requires the science of photosynthesis to mature themselves. I felt the surf of memory once more breaking on the shore of my mind, turning pebbles of detail with endless colours, and then, before it returns to wash the thoughts away, you select a particular shape or colour and study it for a while before deciding to put it in a safe place or, allow it to merge once again from where it first came. The pebble in this case was a corkscrew Hazel, giving to me by a fellow green fingered being. I caressed the stem and eased off its young leaves before allowing it abruptly to sample the delights of hormone rooting compound. Now ready for manhood, it was given the necessary TLC so as not to make it feel unloved and rejected, so important to the young achiever now it had been introduced to the emotions of reproduction, and soon all was well, new shoots did sprout and the proud young parent showed with glee its offspring.

As in so many files of the human mind box when one file is opened, its closely indexed relations are briefly in view. So it was now as I considered my dealings with an Avocado stone. It had been given a soak of warm water, had three pins inserted at as close to equal angles of one hundred and twenty degrees on a horizontal plane around its base, then left to dangle its feet in a jar of tap water. After several weeks waiting, a bit, I suppose, like the plant kingdoms equivalent of an outpatients appointment at your local hospital, signs of action became apparent. A root sprouted and made a dash for the bottom of the jar whereby it was diverted back up and around and forced to follow this course until relieved by transplantation. This would only take place once it was considered the plant could cope with being separated from its clinical existence and allowed the familiar surroundings that felt like home, namely John Innes compost and a comforting terracotta pot, with plenty of liquids for good measure. Unfortunately, as in our own realm, sometimes the goodness of help and the reassurance of encouragement, in the end can be no more than a comfortable hammock between the trees of life and death.

So it was that the Avocado took up membership of the great fruit parlour in the sky.

It was but a piece of old rusty wire stretched between two posts but it was enough to kick-start a train of thought on the subject of telephone boxes. Don't ask me why, it just seemed to be next in the queue of electrical pulses hiding behind the curtain of recovery in the stage door of my brain, ready to don its facial expression whilst in the wings before entering stage right and, on cue, heading towards its marked position in the drama or comedy that, for one performance only, unless invited back, would now entertain its audience before it.

I like the old telephone boxes, I have never owned one, and wouldn't want to, yet I feel comfortable with them. Maybe it's an English thing that one has had, over the course of ones life and through its many appearances, via media or personal experiences a subliminal connection to its qualities and restrictions. Like, I suspect, many people, I have never questioned its purpose, whether or not it was the best of ideas or if it should have taken another form, it just was always there. Maybe because our most interesting emotions happen in our younger years, perhaps ages one through to four of the seven ages of a man that we cover over or simply ignore any need to be involved in the assessment of such matters.

Shortly after, one has the realisation put before him that he can, to varying degrees affect this and that and if not careful can get caught in the whirlpools of need to have, may need later, need to know more about, is this all there is to know about, who has control over what, why are they there, etc., and must therefore know in himself where to take the helm or simply switch to autopilot and assume someone else is responsible. Perhaps it's like architecture, you either like some style or you don't, but that's a whole new play currently undergoing first dress rehearsal and not ready for opening night.

From the slightly upward gaze my view drifted gently down and fell on a surface that my brain needed to update its files on due to the split second that it took to assess what it was looking at. The processed data revealed not a misshapen flat rock, but a paving slab with numerous small soft mounds along its edges, forming a kind of tepee hedge between it and its neighbours. The mounds were caused by an ant equivalent of inner city redevelopment, where numerous roads and constructions replace what used to be the earthworms local, the spiders library and maybe the old chain of beetles retail outlets. Now in their place mock names, trying in vain to connect with the past, were being given to these new super fast and crowded districts. "Derek Worm" courtyard, "George Snail" rest, and possibly "Harvey B's Bowling Alley. That's ants for you! Suppose I was to find a large flat bottomed stone and place it quietly overnight in the middle of one of the slabs. Would the first ant risers see, in the early morning light, this strange huge new monolith suddenly appeared from nowhere. Would they scamper back to the others and try, in their now hysterical state to explain that aliens had somehow moved Ayres Rock had landed it on the outskirts of their town. Eskimos have about fifty different names for snow, so maybe it wouldn't be 'Ayres Rock' or 'Aliens' but simply 'Habnes Goj' and' rudlakcue'.

Maybe I should knock all their crass mounds down in

retaliation, and on behalf of the united small creature underground movement or 'USCUM' for short. I wonder if they have already infiltrated various colonies and are, as I speak, planning the final stages of assault upon the main chamber where his excellency the mighty 'Dasfud Wombid' is believed to be in hiding.

Maybe, instead, they would hire a very expensive and steel nerved ant barrister to take me to the European Garden Court of Insect Rights and sue me for every penny. Yeah?, well come on then, let's get it on!

The logic of reason which in this case prevented a possible fisticuffs, and almost certainly casualties, was a small yet very ladylike bunch of Bluebells. They had decided to settle on the edge of the underground town and ignoring its surroundings and populous inners, had, like a group of spinsters living in one house, cast their own values higher than that of the surrounding area and decided that no matter what hardships would prevail, that they would not only survive, but pass on some of their own values and beliefs, a kind of Baldwin sisters girl power. I suspect that as in the case of the Baldwin sisters, Moonshine played an invisible yet crucial part in helping various negotiations with the underground movement fall in favour of the Bulbuls. Perhaps one such debate or 'arrangement' was over proposed root planning for the coming season and priority of moisture retention rights. Maybe a record number of work days were lost due to an unusually high ratio of hangovers among the workforce.

I bid the ladies good day and I may have imagined it but I'm sure one of them turned to the side and blushed.

Chapter Two

I took my cue from Mrs Blackbird, now alerting me to the fact I was nearing the point at which friendship becomes annoyance and that though pleased to see me, certain jobs had to be done, in this case preparations for this year's nest building, and, more importantly at present, the ritual daily worm dance and the grub seeking mission.

Most birds would be patient with me, but I understood her need to complete the task in earnest, for this particular Mrs Blackbird was not only the present worm tracking champion, but through her well respected knowledge of the local terrain, had an envious following.

On top of this, as part of this year's local bird elections, Mrs Blackbird had been made aware of the fact that the 'Pigeon and Starling Party' were planning, if not elected to consider a coalition with the 'Thrush and Sparrow Party'. Mrs Blackbird was not a lady to settle for second best, a point made most clearly during last year's annual bird fete.

Mr Rook the Chairman of the seasons Hedge Council, along with Jessica Finch and Barty Barn Owl (yes that's his real name!) were judging the best 'Regurgitated Berry

Pie'. Mr Alan Magpie, the champion collector three years running was excluded from this years events on grounds of insanity, since trying to offer 'Henrietta Heron' up as the most original similarity to a garden ornament.

The afternoon was beginning to draw to a sleepy conclusion, and matters weren't helped by a pitiful effort to liven things up by Charlie Sparrow resurrecting many an old joke and even trying to test a few new ones. As his weary audience were not quite as streetwise as himself and didn't understand the theory or practicality of a four stroke engine, his comparison between the Woodpecker family and the Reliant Robin went completely over their heads. In fact, the only response was a somewhat pointed reply from the Magpie clan who by now were quite light headed through their consumption, and mixing of, unripe berries and a suspicious home-brew, the recipe of which was known only to themselves.

Having the sense to know when he was beaten, Charlie Sparrow announced the judging in the grand final of the 'Regurgitated Berry Pie' contest was about to begin. Mrs Blackbird proudly displayed her offering and confidently waited the result.

Her disbelief at the announcement that Wendy Sedgewarbler was the winner was only contained by a request for an independent second opinion. Tawny Giles, head of night-time security was called in and within minutes, had discovered a now foiled plot. It was revealed that Miss Wendy Sedgewarbler, through a misguided sense of loyalty to the shunned Mr Alan Magpie, had made the mixture, not in her gullet, but from seeds and rotten leaves, with a dollop of slug trail thrown in for good measure, an ornithological equivalent of television vomit. With head under wing Wendy Sedgewarbler was escorted away and the honour of triumph was passed to Mrs Blackbird.

This level of determination and attention to detail was finding its way into the feathered community, and now nearly all of the time, at some stage or another, she would be followed and watched, at a safe distance, by young up and coming hopefuls who wished that one day they too would taste the sweetness of glory.

I acknowledged her request and calmly walked away. At a sensible distance I turned to politely wish her well, but she was gone. Good Luck Mrs Blackbird.

I had noticed an unusual form when I first came down the side path. Now with the garden opening up before me, I was confronted by the sight of it again, sitting there, waiting as if in some time frozen trance. Could it still be here? A deeply buried forgotten memory bud sprouted up through to the forefront of my mind, literally taking my breath away.

I had to find out, I had to know. My heart decided it was time for a more Latin American beat, and with fumbling feet I crept up to it. I was fearful of it springing a nasty surprise on me, not a physical attack, no, this time it would be an emotional shock, a bit like mending the Christmas tree lights; just as you think you're fully prepared and have mended all the faults, a blast of 240 volts goes shooting up your arm. Although there is a physical discomfort as well,

it is the completely overriding sense of embarrassment and shock that gives the reaction such a powerful and immediate effect of helplessness.

No one I have ever met who has suffered this fate can remember the details of their reaction.

One tries to explain oneself, tries to give cause to the effect, tries to salvage one's pride. So it was now, a brief triggered response gave way to an awkward feeling of insecurity, of worry, of fear.

Quite why a child's tractor should emote such feelings I couldn't answer. I tried pathetically to cover up my now stripped shell of pretence as I lost the battle with a wave of emotion that finally pushed me and made me realise that that time had passed, and I began to cry.

I struggled to find something that would slap me round the face and pull me out of my mood. Eventually I convinced myself that the glasshouse would warrant an investigation, so wiping my eyes and nose in one continual movement, I regrouped my physical and mental self and worked out a plan of attack. As it happened, it required no force, other than the initial forward movement, because as I walked towards, and drew closer to, the glasshouse, I had the same feeling that comes at the end of a really good film or drama, when on comes the irritating voice of the continuity announcer, taking you from one detached plan of involvement, to an annoying temporary period of commercials, before the next choice of viewing which, more often than not, includes the choice, not to watch.

I decided to switch to another mind channel. Luckily it wasn't a repeat, but an interesting item on personal pride. The glass, like the pointing in the brickwork and the rusty door hinges, had seen better days and had decided to join the 'Modern Day Fallouts', or M.D.F. for short. Once strong and orderly, this brotherhood of glass, aluminium, wood, brick and soil, now resembled a cross between a Wendy house, and how my hair looks in the morning.

Clinging onto a piece of respect for the past, it allowed the door to be opened, but, to save face, only with a good deal of shoulder work and the accompanying sound that a door makes when being slowly sanded on a concrete slab. Luckily, I could rise to this cheap effort to convert me to its now more sombre state, and I warmly remembered its construction, the tightening of bolts, the laying in of the glass, and the smell, ah the smell, of fresh putty as it was rolled and pushed into place by palm and thumb. Then finally, to fulfil its purpose, the growing of various salad plants and fruit that were harvested with that self satisfied feeling of accomplishment. Now I was remembering more smells, freshly wetted soil, green plant growth, the kind of smells you only get in sheds and greenhouses, and then, best of all, the taste of the produce. Crunchy lettuce, juicy tomatoes, clean watery cucumbers and sweet, sweet strawberries. I pulled the door to, and with it, another more restful remembrance.

Isn't it funny how when you twist your ankle you get the same feeling as when you are confronted by a drunk person. For an instant you are not sure how to react, then you either add humour to the situation and begin a contorted laugh, or realise things could get interesting and adjust your body language accordingly. I now felt the first of these two as I walked over not so much as a divot, but more of a concave scoop that was playing peekaboo with any unsuspecting wanderer in the long grass. Perhaps this was revenge for the Pampas grass that had once been there and had been so awkwardly removed and cremated.

No one was applauding or joining in the laughter, so realising I had suffered in vain, I now made the best of maintaining a steady if not slightly limped step back towards the rear of the house. I was pulled, as if by magnet, over to the corner of the house and once passed the solid of the wall, set off on a course where a wide driveway should have been.

Odd tufts of grass, freely growing unpruned Budleia bushes, and other various untamed plants of numerous descriptions were trying to disguise the driveway behind their camouflage, but like the sun behind a passing cloud, the deception is only temporary, and various clues lead to its position.

A crunching sound underfoot affirmed that that particular cloud had passed and now the sun was back in its place. Like a newly revealed army of randomly positioned terracotta warriors, the shaped stones gave the area purpose and put it into context.

In their predictable places, the obligatory specks of black oil and, a few yards further down the spent exhaust fuel droplets filled in the details.

I was tempted to go off on a mental tangent and start dissecting the social needs and outcomes that the car has been involved in, and the many possible avenues of thought concerning our needs to feel fulfilled and safe when amongst strangers, namely other drivers, and how, as the millennium approached, we relied more and more on the one thing that we had at the same time used as a scapegoat for our own frustrations, and comfortably blamed for the state of our environment, but, instead of going round that roundabout of many possible exits, I turncd left at the lights of reason and continued down a lane of more homely and pleasant vistas.

I turned off onto a track that wound down before me and allowed the potholes of thought to rock my car of memories from side to side while I steered what I considered to be, on average, the most productive route.

On the subject of potholes, well almost, why do people go potholing? What makes them want to crawl through impossibly tight gaps between millions of tons of rock, then after getting seriously wet in freezing mud and water, turn around and find what they hope is the way out again. I was on the point of labelling them as insane when I, as a man who likes to trim the edges of a lawn with a pair of household scissors, concluded that I had no place in doing so.

A slight breeze was beginning to make itself known, and announcing its arrival, a feather, minus its previous owner, gently drifted downwards until it came to rest upon a spiders web that was keeping the window frame from collapsing. I thought of all the millions of other now discarded feathers, through natural wastage rather than hopefully foul means, and that if by a chance of nature, (whose odds would have to make the National Lottery seem like a game of 'Find The Lady'), they were all to blow into one pile, say on a hill on the Isle of Wight, would they create an enormous but very comfortable pillow? The Americans have their Umpire State Building, the Canadians have the Niagara Falls, and so on, why couldn't we have are own equivalent of Alcatraz Island but call it Pillow Island, or Feather Pile National Park. Think of all the business that could come from it. Boats from all the mainland ports on the south coast offering 'Pillow day trips' or, local residents come guides could take people round and show tourists where the great gangster' Legs Flea The Biter' once hatched an escape, or the little corner that for nearly a decade was home for 'Birdman Lice'. Then what if Hollywood showed an interest and made a film about the place. Dale Winton could lead a troop of men onto the island and the film could be called 'The Soft Rock'.

This particular feather remained attached to the spiders web, when another thought came to me. I wonder if the spiders have their own arachnid parish or town councils and that every Tuesday morning they meet in their chambers behind the air brick and discuss various items of local importance. Perhaps this week Eddie Rackshaw, their resident and very busy cobbler, would be voicing his opinion on the failure of the Environment Department, and their meagre efforts, to clear up the constant stream of waste paper and plastic products that endlessly blow across, and block many of the local residents pathways. The Environment Departments argument that this kind of clean up operation would require an outside contractor, namely the human species, would fall on deaf ears, well no ears really, and after a suitable period of 'Here Here's and 'Members, Please', a motion to defer the debate until more evidence was assessed would be agreed upon and satisfied members would then take their discussions to the bar next door and sample the delights of the locally brewed and particularly strong 'Old Fly Swat'.

Chapter Three

Back round the rear of the house a sound similar to that of fingernails on a blackboard took my ears. As I turned back and leaned my body so that only my head was visible to whatever it was, the sound drew my inquisitive searching eyes to an old galvanised watering can that, owing to its rounded bottom, both on the vertical and horizontal planes, was rocking awkwardly, and by pressing on various stones, pieces of clay pot and cement, was causing a rather annoying grating noise. Like when a plate or coin refuses to fall flat until they have performed numerous never ending spins, the same impatient waiting had to be suffered before it would rest. When at last it came to rest and the cause of the movement, namely a shabby looking cat, had run off after the appearance of a decapitated head hovering six feet above ground level, I felt obliged to make its acquaintance. Picking it up by its still strong handle, its spout bowed in a gesture of acceptance and gently rocked back in a polite gentlemanly manner. Still proud of its bodies condition, and rightly so, I could feel the underlying cheerfulness it felt at being used again and was most grateful that I had accepted yet not mentioned its now restricted uses, part due to being abandoned and part the contents of its inside namely a handful of last year's leaves, some small stones and at least an inch of silty mud.

How many times had we as a team help to water thirsty plants, fill birdbaths and child size watering cans. Like an old soldier preparing for a parade, I helped to clean his uniform, empty and rinse his inside, polish his shoes and put on a freshly cleaned berry, namely its copper rose. As he stood there proud and rejuvenated, at least for a while, I honoured him with an inspection before silently saluting him and ordering him to stand easy.

I found myself playing a form of the old psychiatrists favourite of 'What comes into your head when.....', and after being given the topic of water, meandered onto a bigger picture.

I wonder if when the creator of this earth, for arguments sake we'll call him God, developed the oceans and seas, and played around with the positions of the sun and moon, he realised that along with the tides, waves would be created too and that in turn surf would prevail. Maybe it was an unexpected bonus that was a pleasant surprise, and as it fitted in with things so nicely he decided to keep them. Maybe he got a late sale bargain from the universe equivalent of MFI and the surf was thrown in as an incentive to buy, from the sales manager. Maybe the trees and flowers came 'Direct To Your Planet!' from the space version of a garden centre or B&Q Depot.

What actually are waves and surf for? We know how they are caused and the ingredients that make them, but is there a purpose to them other than satisfying the needs of people who by some incredible coincidence are called 'surfers'?

What if those people were called 'Bin Dudes'? They would have to leave the beaches and find alleyways and industrial parks in search of, not the best wave, but the best, most street-cred, dustbin. Suburbia could latch onto the trend and would sprout new forms of 'one upmanship' with the 'Smiths' opting for an environmentally friendly paisley check pattern with acidic green lid, while the 'Joneses' would go for the Volvo approach and have a heavy duty box shaped bin with the lid slightly offset, allowing, by accident of course, a pair of green Hunter wellies to be visible.

My curiosity needed a prey and so with imaginary coin in hand I chose G5 on my jukebox of options and walked in a curved line back down through the now heavy undergrowth and aimed for a spot somewhere in front of the far boundary hedge. At a hither to unseen small clearing my step was halted by a large square piece of dark and rotten wood, probably an old table top, though the whereabouts of its legs and frame remained a mystery.

Feeling slightly more confident now with my new found explorers freedom I couldn't help indulging myself in a child like curiosity, and, lowering myself down onto all fours and then twisting and lowering my head further, I lifted the cold and mouldy slab of timber to allow me a look underneath.

The scene before me reminded me of a turn of the century working class back street. Along with the usual centipede or two scurrying away like a pair of dodgy dealers, and a few tiny slugs resigned to their new upside down existence, were an entire community of woodlouse living in rather squalid conditions but making the best of it. Like a group of workers wives, each one seeming to have somewhere to go, something to do, all looking the same, all trying to keep the homesteads together by their individual needs and circumstance. The strong arms, the rounded backs, the purpose to their monotonous tasks, the dull and dreary existence, yet time for gossip and a laugh. Then at the end of the husbands day, stood on the doorstep, arms crossed, waiting for him to come home enjoying the local neighbourhood news about Batty Albright's latest 'doings'. Another last warning shout for the 'Brats' to come in for their tea, and then closing the door on one unfair world to suffer another. I don't think the women could roll themselves up into an armoured ball like the woodlice, I have no hard evidence either way, but I still enjoyed my glimpse of their world, and with a caring slowness lowered the piece of wood, then, using a hand on top of my knee for leverage, raised myself .

Not having seen the protruding post or its occupant, a four inch rusty nail, my curse was one of shock rather than pain, and as I consoled and gently rubbed my shin which was now mass marketing the hurt effect I chose not to begin hopping like an entrant in some parent day school race but instead allowed the pain to subside where I stood. After a few minutes the only evidence of the assault was a mere graze and a fine two inch line of dried blood.

This blunt reminder that I was now in unfamiliar territory prompted me to find something that I could lay claim to, something I could recognise, touch, be a friend with once more. I kept urgency from my situation by calmly turning around and mentally adjusting the proportions of the place until they fitted the original blueprint that was being unrolled in my head. Like a navigator trying to allow for wind and tide I compensated for various factors, some easy, some tricky, and some a best guestimate.

With my now updated x-ray view of the place I began to diagnose various symptoms like a retired GP. Slowly things made sense, some were new to me, some old favourites and I congratulated myself on a satisfactory prognosis.

I had made a mental note of one or two things that I wanted to check out later, but for now I turned and headed for the side of the garden, the sloping side that had once revealed by way of a deliberately staggered hedge a grand and honoured view across the tops of the trees in the woods below and onward out towards the distant hues of the sea. Like a remembered child's toy from your childhood, size colour and detail get fondly distorted through time and so it was now with the wood below now no more than a copse of young hazel, and the panorama of the oceanic horizon a mere space between two houses.

If, like choosing a colour of paint, you could choose a particular time, place, or subject, would you choose the same today as you chose once before, long ago?

Would what was fashionable and contemporary then be just as important now? Perhaps like architects and painters, we either like to move and evolve trends and styles, or, we try to keep alive easier, more comfortable surroundings that we have gotten used to.

The jury was still out on what I was now. The case for my defence had batted admirably and argued many a good point with keen sometimes soft, sometimes aggressive vocation. On the other hand, as with many an underdog, what was once looked upon as worthless and menial, now rose in great style through the smooth and cleverly constructed case for the prosecution which had gripped the attention of all concerned. I await their verdict. I hope it's the right one.

Like a fumbling actor who has missed his cue for 'exit stage left', I knew it was time to leave the scene but couldn't work out how.

Feeling ready enough to face what the critics of hindsight may say, I took the chance before me and left the stage. Not looking at any of the other performers, nor caring if I perchance, knocked into a prop or two, for my head position was set, my gaze aimed at an invisible wall some ten feet into the wings, and shutting out the play before me I 'exited stage left' in what I considered to be a swift and stylish fashion.

I tried putting myself in the audiences position, trying to work out what they thought, but in true human characteristic they were probably doing the same to me, neither of us wanting to find out by asking for fear of losing face, happy to contend with an empty assumption that each was the more relaxed with the situation. I calmly made my way back to the house.

The pebble dashed rendering was showing signs of tarnish and here and there minor cracks were appearing, reminding me of an elderly lady who has trowelled on the makeup with the intention of either doing a facial equivalent of a sandwich board walker advertising a building material, or thinking that we other mere mortals couldn't possibly tell the difference between soft, clean skin, and quick drying cement floor paint.

I started to wonder how pebbledash came about. Maybe it

started with one labourer picking up some gravel and throwing it at his mate in a form of a builders bun fight, and the stones then landing in a freshly rendered piece of wall, so that when the contractor came upon it, it was assumed to be a new form of exterior decor, which because it looked so good, and, because it was then shown to perspective purchasers as the latest fashion in exterior wall coverings, the trend literally stuck, and soon houses across the land were being given the same 'trendy' facing. I wonder what would have been the 'norm' if that first labourer had thrown a cheese and pickle sandwich!

The guttering above was still trusting its fixings in the fascia board to hold it out from the house. Do you think that leaves and pieces of moss form queues on the top of the roof, and at a predetermined moment, namely a heavy downpour, they race each other to be first into the guttering, and like children in a water chute at an amusement park, go hurtling along until, with shrieks of excited fear, they go plunging into the dark down pipe, They fall almost endlessly until suddenly they are shot out into the daylight again where they can take a brief pause in the hopper before again tumbling down another darkened tube, only this time, instead of surfacing in a large warm pool, they are cruelly taken further down and forced round many twists and tunnels before joining other similar folk from other water parks, and then joining stems or fronds, and in true British style, face their maker to a hearty rendition of' Rule Britannia'.

Higher still, on the roof itself, the grey slates laying like scales on a fish, reflected not vibrant rainbow like colours, but a sense of trust, of reliability, and with its dorsal fin of chimney and pot, set against a now monochromatic sky, the scene was that of a Mullet slowly cruising the shallows of a drying estuary, meandering around with an occasional glimpse of a white mouth.

I imagined dozens of aliens hovering in correctly marked out spaceships along the edge of a town or city, all with ingeniously crafted extraterrestrial fishing rods, dangling huge chunks of star bread or crater cheese, waiting, waiting and hoping for a prize winning catch.

Suddenly a roof would close in on the bait, adrenaline levels would rise, and then in that decisive moment it would amble away. Then as if from nowhere a bigger, more daring roof, say that from a hotel or conference centre, would dart across, open its gable and snatch the bait with a heart stopping whop.

The reflex would have to be instantaneous as the alien would struggle to play the now frantic roof up and down the street, teasing it away from snags such as overhanging power cables and bridges, slowly tiring it until that tense moment when it would be secured aboard, with that sense of tired emotive release that made the waiting worthwhile. At the end of the days contest, the various roofs would be weighed and prizes awarded. No doubt someone would be disqualified for trying to enter an undersized specimen such as a shed or public convenience. Finally, the grand prize of a new retractor beam would be given to last years winner who again knew just where the right spot seemed to be. Rumours, and I stress just rumours would be put about that he had an insider on the local planning committee of the town council. Whatever reason, he would have his picture taken for the 'Neptune Chronicle' and

'Roofing Angler' before taking him or her or itself off with his fellow competitors for a jug or two of astro juice at the local planetary hostelry.

Adjusting my now aching neck back down to a more level horizon and waiting a suitable period of a second or two to allow my balance to correct itself, I continued on around the corner of the path and adjusted my conscious vision to the data before me.

It dawned on me that what I was looking at was not the front of this houses hedge, but the back of next door's hedge. The new lush growth of spring had taken hold and was slowly changing this spindly mish-mash of twigs into a smooth green texture which would define its shape and relevance in the place it was growing.

If you were say, the size of a field mouse, or if indeed you were a dormouse, what a great time you could enjoy by exploring all the nooks and crannies of, what to you, would be like a massive tropical forest. You would enter one side all confident, clean shaven and crisply dressed, and slowly as the hours passed you would become clammy, hot, tired, and fed up with having to contort yourself round logs and branches of varying size. You would either go mad and crack up or, finally when hunger is begging you to feed it, you find the way out and reach the other side. You relax, congratulate yourself on your achievement and are all ready to rest and unwind, when you realise you have left your Thermos flask and medical kit back on the other side, and now you are faced with having to go through all that again. It's enough to break the toughest of field mice into snivelling fur balls.

Chapter Four

At the bottom of the hedge there is a flower. A single delicate little blue flower on an even more delicate stem. Its basal leaves compliment it by gently bending outwards from its base giving it a raise appearance. The blue of the petals is like you see on seaside beach huts, that light blue that has no name yet all the huts come in varying shades of it. It is not pretentious, or gaudy, just simple, clean, elegant and sweet.

I need not approach it, for it is best seen from where I stand. I need not pick it, for that would kill it. I need not smell it, for it exudes its own perfume. I exchange pleasantries and bid it good day. It was reassuring to come across something so pleasant, easily at home, with an air of ordered grace, amongst all the confusion that was all around me.

This glimpse of normality helped me to adjust and remember the position of a tree stump that I had passed on my way down to the end of the garden. It was easy to retrace my steps, by simply stepping into the trodden and sunken pieces of grass and stick. There, with its flat head just peering over its skyline of brambles, weeds and other growth was a slim but stout base of what once must have been a fruit tree. Being a tactile person where trees are concerned, I felt the urge to examine this specimen closer. Its bark though hideously contorted by bad pruning and natural ageing felt uncannily smooth. I parted the long grass and peered at the small eco-climate at its base. There I saw ants and tiny black beetles scurrying around like misshapen bumper cars, colliding with each other, or simply doing seven point turns or spinning uncontrollably. They seemed to be acting out a scene from 'Journey to the centre of the earth', the one where they encounter giant mushrooms before they are face to face with a giant monster breathing down on them. The final showdown is where the rocks and temple start to crumble and fall dangerously near before they, at the last moment, find sanctuary in an enormous bowl which spews them up to the fastly approaching escape hole. What had actually happened was, on leaning down to invade their world, my hand had began the earthquake by crumbling the rotten wood and sending it raining down on them in numerous pieces. The life saving bowl was actually an old blue button that I had picked up to examine and had only noticed when I was raising it, that it was occupied by two black beetles and an ant.

Time called for their world to be saved and I gently returned them and their surroundings to as close as I could get it, how it was before their adventure had began.

I hate pigeons. They always seem to have some kind of air about them, as if we as humans should respect them, the way Indians do cattle. Maybe they're right, but I have seen no news to substantiate that idea, so, for now, I hate them.

A brace were now flying Spitfire fashion around me in large loops on a circular course. Eventually they did me the 'honour' of stopping to rest in the top branches of a nearby chestnut tree. Even out of sight I recognised the soulless 'hoo-hooing' of their vocabulary.

Town pigeons, the kind to adorn Lord Nelson or any city monument seem to at least have a streetwise attitude to them, and I can respect them for that, but these more rural kind, in particular the common Wood pigeon seem to serve no purpose other than eating corn and annoying people. Perhaps when and if the day of judgement comes I might be faced with the High Council of Pigeons in their assessment of my life on earth, and they may agree unanimously to crawl around on the pavements of cities, jumping out of the way as huge pigeons walk by. The other further embarrassment I would have to endure would be to have to do my ablutions and other lavatorial duties in public. I await my fate.

This particular pair were beginning to annoy me so, by giving the appearance of splatting invisible flies between two flattened palms, I began making loud singular clapping sounds, but this merely seemed to rile me further and them smugger. Eventually they did me the graceful thing and with a rapid fire of wing flap, took off to annoy some other unsuspecting creature.

My pride restored, I again started to study the present time and scene.

Laid on its side and angled against the overlapping boards of the fence was an unwanted two piece wooden ladder. It looked like an instrument from a scene in Bedknobs and Broomsticks, the scene towards the end when the enemy are invading, and a magic spell brings hoards of suits of armour and fighting instruments to life. Eventually the spell is broken and all the ghostly pieces fall back down to the ground. The ladder, with its own spell broken, looked like one of these pieces, and instead of being triumphantly paraded up to the front line, had decided to swap roles and now play the role of a sleeping beauty, being gently but steadily covered by growth all around. Well, I'm no Gueilgood or genius, but I felt compelled to break the spell, and working through long grass, slowly pulling away runners from a blackberry bush, cutting a swathe through the plants with my wooden 2" x 1" sword I boldly approached the damsel princess. Eventually I arrived at her sleeping quarters, and leaned over and offered her a kiss to lift the curse. Gently working my hands and my arm under and around her shoulders, I began to raise the sleepy princess up to my waist, being careful not to tear her clothing and making note of the haute couture label of Jewson.

I continued to raise her up to my shoulders then further again, for this was one long legged princess, until she gazed down at all before her, and, as if she had momentarily dropped off instead of asleep for years, uttered words so soft and gentle, so regal and pure, namely "right, where's the bucket and sponge, and don't you be dallying with that paintbrush or we won't be home tonight". I answered in words that seemed fitting, "right away your highness". The side effects of having been asleep for sometime kicked in, and like an aftershock following an earthquake I could tell she needed rest, so I gently laid her back down, carefully making sure no sharp stones would annoy her although I was quite confident I hadn't missed many, this after all, being sleeping beauty and not the 'Princess and the Pea'.

While she lay sleeping I tucked her in, with the long grass and weeds gently forming her pillows and blanket. I hope she wouldn't have to sleep as long this time, and as I moved quietly away on tiptoe, she gave a large draw of breath before sighing gently as she entered her world of dreams.

Proportionally, the little shed was correct, but what was out of proportion was the now hideously overgrown bush that enveloped it on three sides leaving a hint of a window and the makings of a door. The high boundary wall was the only thing offering any resistance to the forces of the bush's growth, and in reply to this rebuff the bush had decided to make its point far stronger than it normally would have.

Now peeking out of its enclosed world the little shed seemed to have resigned to its fate, in much the same way a goldfish does when being plopped into its bowl or tank for the first time. Like the goldfish, the shed would remain its present size in its dimensioned world, and in a sad way had accepted its lot.

The urge to go in and have a rummage was strong, so instead of tapping the glass of a fish tank, I knocked on the door and offered an incomprehensible greeting before turning the Bakerlite door knob. Assuming the door would oblige and swing on its rusty hinges, I was taken back when the door simply fell forward into the shed causing a skirting of dust to curl up either side.

I now had an awkwardly placed slope of timber to negotiate back up to the doorway before turning it on its corner and leaning it temporarily against its acquired big brother. I tentatively lowered my head slightly and stepped inside.

Once inside I was like a child in a sweet shop, although in my case it would have to have been a fishing tackle shop, as in those days, being an enthusiastic young angler, I preferred maggots to Mars bars.

I remembered warmly the early Saturday mornings waiting outside for the shop to open. Rods and tackle had already been checked, and with sandwiches and flask of tea already prepared, all that was required was the bait.

The large two thirds glazed door would echo the sound of rattling keys and be opened, along with that unmistakable sound of an old sprung operated doorbell, and a cheery welcome, by the shopkeeper.

On entering, the experience of a dozen generations would exude from the large smooth and worn bare floorboards and the three long mahogany framed, glaze topped counters. All around you, on racks, in cabinets, and in the counters themselves would be rods, reels, nets, and rows of shiny spinners, weights, floats, literally everything, you thought, you would need. After deciding it might be wise to get just one more three quarter ounce 'Arsley Bomb' weight and a No. 3 Mepps spinner, you allowed yourself the expression of a contented expert as you asked either of the two friendly faced shopkeepers for your requirements.

In one smooth movement you made your request by pointing with the left hand, and simultaneously passing across the empty bait box with your right. As one man would get the weight and spinner out from under the thick and finely scratched glass counter top, offering a congratulatory comment on their suitability for the local waters, the other man would disappear into the back of the shop before returning with a pint of maggots sealed in their container.

The tackle and bait box would be handed over in exchange for the weeks pocket money, and after an advisory mention from either side of the counter, three smiling faces would part company, one to the back of the shop, one to attend to stock and one to the path leading to the river.

For four or five hours I would sit on the bank casually deciding whether to change from float to spinner, or from 'ledgering' on the bottom with the weight to a mere baited hook flowing freely just under the surface.

Often, after only two or three hours I could be seen walking back up through the town with stories of broken lines, large clumps of weed that ate my weights, or possible giants that must have been the only cause to my now broken rod tip.

Inside the shed the lovely musty smell complemented the numerous items around me. Apart from the few marks that the door had made when falling over, everything was covered in a fairy sprinkled mix of dust, cobwebs and a delicate blanket of fine wool-like growth that always accompanies these scenes.

All the various shapes and surfaces had succumbed to this mummification process and had taken the appearance of a well rotted bowl of fruit. Edges had merged, sizes equalised, and to an untrained eye, the scene would be considered a lost cause. But I knew that underneath, things would be practically untouched.

Okay, so some of the tools may need rubbing with wire wool, and some of the paint tins would now contain thick skinned and lumpy, if not totally congealed paint; but also a secondary set of images would be there. Loose wood shavings, oil stains from an oil stone in its box, a carpenters pencil, soil from a plant pot, and, now tattered, cotton rags. Above all, it still had an essence, an essence of how a workshop, irrelevant of size, should feel, should smell, should be.

Some of the items I recognised, Some I had forgotten, Some I never knew were there. The little window with its corners rounded by fragile spiders webs, offered a romantic and fond view of what used to be a calm and restful place. It tried its best now, but like the bush around it, factors outside its control had reshapen its outlook. Above the window, little shelves that made up part of the sheds frame, held small items like coins, pencils, an often used spanner, and tiny cube boxes of brass tacks, self tapping screws, and panel pins.

On the bench before me, an old saw handle made itself known to me along with a pocket tape measure, two jars of jellified white spirit, and a metal box. Taking the rusty edged lid off the box, I realised I had stirred more memories of some time ago. Looking up at me, as if to say 'About time!', were six packets of mixed flower seeds and a figure of eight ball of gardeners twine. I felt very guilty as I explained to them that this wasn't 'their time' after all, and to be patient for some day soon, they would be placed in fresh damp soil to burst into life. I didn't have the heart to tell them the truth, that they had in fact gone well past their 'usefulness' dates, and that they would probably never experience the joys and pure pleasure of germination. With a helpless smile, I put the lid back on the box, and with it their dreams, and turned away slap sliding the rusty dust from my hands.

I had momentarily forgotten that a sheds roof lowers as it goes back, so as to allow the rain to drain off. I was reminded of this simple fact by scraping the top of my head on one of the ceiling joists. After a reflex action of ducking, and, at the same time, rubbing my head, I slowly raised my head on whose face was the expression of someone sucking a lemon, and was confronted by a rusty top half of a four in nail which had been hammered into another of the joists in front of me.

Like some elaborate jungle warfare booby-trap system, I tried to move this way and that, but was prevented from doing so by an ever increasing number of possible snares. It was then I had the feeling that the shed was closing in on me, by not allowing me the correct amount of movement in relation to the size of the space I was standing in.

I awkwardly manoeuvred myself, while at the same time doing an impression of someone being attacked by a swarm of bees, back towards the door until finally,

whilst now also looking like a loyal bowing butler on overdrive, I threw myself out of the doorway back into a more airy place, namely the outside.

Like a once tried fairground ride I wanted to go back and go in the shed again, but, for the moment, I would save my fifty pence ride for later.

I brushed the dust and laces of cobweb downwards off my shoulders, shirt and trousers before reassessing my head wound, which, as it turned out was very superficial. No matter how many times I searched and prodded my hair and scalp with my fingers, only the tiniest specks of blood were to be seen at any one time. Like a boy with a cut knee who expected, at least, stitches to such an appalling injury, I had to accept the outcome with a degree of disappointment, as, in this case, the shed window show my reflection, and like the voice of a accident-wise staff nurse, reassured me that it was only a scratch, and not to worry. Maybe next time!

Chapter Five

To the right of the shed down at ground level, were a stack of old clay pots of similar size, bending slightly at the top, giving them a Tower of Pisa effect. By their side a small mound of rocks, obviously alien to this garden, which presumably had been put there for some future use. As in their creation, time was of no significance, and they quite happily lay there knowing that they would easily outlast the creatures that would eventually come along and move them into their next 'temporary' location.

Butting up to the rocks, were a sad looking pile of roof tiles. The overhanging lower branches of the laurel hedge, as well as the muddy environment that was surrounding them, had given the tiles a hopeless and pointless existence. They would prefer the fresh air blowing over them, the hot sun charging their inner soles, and the sweet fresh rain quenching their thirst, as they lay side by side on a roof somewhere.

Nothing of any importance was immediately following, before I caught sight of a small, more open patch of turfed ground, about four feet by two feet, about fifteen feet away. Why this particular patch had not become the straggly giant like its brothers and sisters I could not immediately work out. Maybe a local group of rabbits used this patch for regular family gatherings, or other social discussion groups. Maybe something was either poured on its surface, or, something sinister was immediately below. Whatever the cause, it gave it an abstruse quality against an otherwise rampaging attack of plant rebellion.

I decided it warranted further investigation and accordingly set about plotting a course, which, although just yards away, required various feats of acrobatic agility, in order to cover the said distance.

I began by straddling a raised iron bar which seemed to be hovering about two feet above the ground. About four feet in length, I could see no means of support either end, but assumed that it would not budge easily enough to be merely pushed out of the way. So, with right leg bent at the knee and thigh raised to an unnatural angle, I transferred body weight to the back leg, before lunging it to the fore, while at the same time lifting the back leg, in the hope of making an invisible arc with my lower regions. The plan should have ended with my right leg landing on firm ground, and taking the now forward moving body weight.

Instead, the crunching, snapping sound hinted at the fact that my right foot had landed in or on something somewhat different from firm ground. This was backed up by a sharp pain that suggested the said 'surface' was trying to impale itself on me.

Scientific fact has the habit of announcing itself at the most obvious times, and, like the reaction to a well worn joke, I was not laughing at it, but accepting it with an irritated tone. The 'joke' this time was the old chestnut about too much weight on one side of a fulcrum will cause an imbalance, with the weighted side falling at the same rate as the unweighted side when it rises.

My groin seemed to have assumed the role of fulcrum, with my right leg being the heavier side. So, to prove scientific fact, I involuntarily acted the theory out.

True to form my left leg lifted itself at an uncomfortable rate whilst my now painful and load bearing right leg had accepted gravity with verve.

After going through a split second of uncertainty, my right leg made touch down, allowing a second scientific theory, regarding the transference of energy and movement, to be tested. My lower back and buttocks being shot sideways, my body automatically accepted its fate and prepared muscles and nerve endings for an uncomfortable conclusion.

Once again, in true fashion, my brain had not allowed an ample supply of numbing fluid to be sent to the appropriate parts, and the vocal department was sent in to announce its disapproval, as my rump and lower back came into contact with an old milk crate.

This collision had taken place at exactly the same time, the 'hovering' iron bar had accepted gravity with open arms, and chosen its landing site, which happened to be the same piece of ground now occupied by my left hip.

The realisation that the situation had reached epic proportions of futility was only contained by a late offering from the corridors of the humour department, which also helped towards dulling the sharp pain in the various parts of my lower anatomy.

Since I had assumed the posture of, and was now a similar

height off the ground as one of our four legged domestic friends, I decided I might as well stay feline, and use this more appropriate character to my advantage, and reach my objective in a more efficient manner than my more clumsy human form.

As I parted the long tufts of grass before me, and made sure my knees didn't press on anything sharp, I crawled along the remaining six or seven feet, not worrying about stained kneecaps or dirty cuffs, but keen to see up close, the grassed area ahead.

When about six away I paused to get a general perspective, before going in for a more detailed examination. On approach, the main feature seemed to be a collection of spiders webs, gently and precisely laid around the edges, as if in some ceremonial official welcome. Feeling like a visiting diplomat, I courteously edged forward and enjoyed sampling the welcome offered.

Now totally unaware of anything going on outside the garden, I indulged my curiosity again and lowered my head, and studied carefully the cobwebs and grass beneath. The symmetrical and octagonal shapes and lines were impressive to say the least.

I considered how much energy, talent, and manufacturing efficiency would have to be engaged in order to create such a complete pattern and structure.

In human terms, I thought of a groundsman pushing one of those white line marking machines, its wheel turning and being constantly covered in the wet chalky paint, applying it evenly and, depending on its user's capabilities and the surface's evenness, creating a neat and regular line pattern across the green swards before him.

If we were to apply the spiders output efficiency and technique to our groundsman, just think of the possibilities. Overnight, provided he was capable of storing, or bodily creating, the required amount of paint or fluid, he could easily cope with six or seven football pitches, and at least three outdoor athletic stadiums.

The grass below the spiders webs felt soft and smooth, cold but dry, not showing any signs of being sat on by bunnies, chewed by creatures of the same ilk, or poisoned by human hands, just happily growing, or rather, not growing, next to its more rampant relations.

Perhaps this was a mutant form of easy maintenance, hard wearing lawn, as yet undiscovered, or perhaps, some secret experiment, soon to be shown at the next Ideal Home Exhibition. Maybe it was just simply the runt of the local grass family, kept securely within the confines of its family homestead.

Like the ending sweet ending to an episode of 'Little House on the Prairie, I found myself sighing and feeling calm and warm inside, in some false sense of well being.

Slowly, I started the transformation back to human form, and bid farewell to the runt and groundsman.

On arriving back on feet, I found I had got up too quickly, and so paused for a moment to allow the blood flow in my head to settle, my balance to adjust, and my vision to adjust to the brighter light around me.

I began to question why I was still here. What purpose could be served by me exploring this place. Was I looking too deeply into the things around me, or was I missing something more obvious. While I pondered on this train of thought, and allowed my inner debating team to weigh the pros and cons of it all, my legs switched to 'Ahead Slow', and I moved across the more open spaces in front of me, in a form of trance, while I awaited the debates conclusions, and from these conclusions, my next actions. Whilst my learned friend for the prosecution was summing up his case for not staying, a last minute surprise witness for the defence burst into the courtroom, and, pleading with 'M'lud' to hear its statement, offered its testimony to the court.

The surprise witness turned out to be a tree. Not some young headline seeking specimen, but an old trusted and respected beast, that had decided that 'things needed to be said', and the record set straight.

Queens Council for the prosecution gracefully allowed the defence to approach the bench, and after some legal 'ping ponging' of terminology had been gone through, 'M'Lud' allowed the evidence to be heard.

As the square peg of the prosecution had its corners rounded, and a more cylindrical shape of fact began to ease into the round hole of justice, the court officials, members of the bar, and public gallery could start to see the intricacies of the case unfold before them, revealing the innocence of the accused, and hinting towards the real culprit. The only person to remain unaffected by the whole scene was the stenographer who efficiently and quietly pressed in the dictation of the court.

The surprise witness was the old apple tree. If you envisage a typical English garden, through rose tinted imagination, there is always an apple tree somewhere.

Like a favoured grandmother, she could be accepted into any harmonious family. Trusted, respected, never questioned. Silent unwavering and very much the matriarch of an English spring.

One could feel safe leaving children unattended around her, know that, with uncanny ease and the kind of style that comes naturally with experience and love, she would entertain them until teatime, or until parents would call them in.

I thought it appropriate to take a break at this stage, to collate the information so far, to try to seek answers or to try to seek places where answers may be.

Not worrying or caring about crushing beetles, being bitten by ants, or smearing slug slime on my trousers, I approached the tree and introduced my self, before lowering myself at her feet, flattening the long grass and flowers at her feet.

I sat under the old tree, put my legs out straight, then crossed them at the ankle.

Then, with hands locked behind my head, I allowed myself the luxury of reclining back against its craggy trunk. After making a few sideways adjustments, to allow for one or two pieces of bark that were digging into my back, I let myself be taken by the wondrous surroundings that I was enjoying.

I offered thanks to the gods of the place, enough for a first class ticket, closed my eyes and drifted through the different side-shows that were now around me.

Now, nearing the hour of noon, a warm and firm breeze started to be felt on my face, in my hair, and across my back where my shirt was buckled, allowing a flow of air to penetrate under. It stimulated the air in the same way that a room feels when dust sheets are lifted off grateful furniture, allowing many natural scents to voice their appreciation.

Freshly mown grass of the park across the road as the driver of the tractor pulls round, in gladiator fashion, the turning blades of the cutters. The wet now exposed mud of the drying harbour as the young ebb starts its turn in the cycle of tides. The damp, green and now full hedgerows, an earthy smell of a nearby wood, farm animals going through their end of day routines.

Ah, how it gives such a reassuring feeling, a sense of belonging and awareness of beauty, how one felt as a child when greeting a favourite aunt or uncle, an inner knowing that, for the time being, life was good, life was sweet.

All around me were plants and objects of different size and textures. Sat low down and amongst all this detail, I felt as if I were the audience at some elaborate orchestral performance.

The tree began to talk to me, her language not of words, but of sounds, of smells, of colours. While she spoke she allowed the wind to conduct the orchestra around her. One sound would begin the next piece, followed by the accompanying instruments. Sometimes a duet, sometimes a solo, sometimes a piece that built up into a hundred instruments.

Beech trees would sound like symbols being gently ground against each other, a birds call like a penny whistle, violins in the form of straining, tall, tough leafed plants. A harp would grace the proceedings whilst in harmony with a 'triangle' of a piece of trapped twig against the fence.

I was totally enthralled by the performance, then when the house lights were brightened and interval announced I felt pleased and at the same time saddened.

An engine from an aircraft high overhead announced the end of the interval, so I stretched my arms above my head, uncrossed then re-crossed my legs, wiggled slightly into my seat, cleared my throat a couple of times, and awaited the second half's performance.

Not quite knowing what to expect, I had assumed more of the same medium to heavy orchestrated sound, but I was pleasantly surprised when the first couple of untitled pieces were of a more graceful and genteel nature.

The soft delicate notes enchanted me and I imagined clouds, primroses, cowslips and blossom. A touch more tubular, metallic sounds came through and brought with it, watercress, blue irises and tadpoles.

The location had changed as well. No more auditoriums or fancy plush theatres, but now a more refined, tasteful and elegant tea-room, or orangery, and at times, on a great lawn before a wide river.

String quintets and exquisite piano music filled most of the afternoon's programme, before the final piece was experienced. There was no big build up, no screaming violins, no masochistic piano keys being pummelled in rhythmic ecstasy, no flapping of the conductor's tailcoat. Instead, a calm, quiet, yet refined haunting aria performed by an unknown vocalist. Its finish was that of sharp ice, 1 clean, pure, cutting and breathtaking. Oh, how in my mind I applauded, silently calling 'Bravo, Bravo'. My soul felt lifted and full to bursting. I imagined myself rising out of my seat and excitedly talking about it all the way across the street and into a packed bar where fellow witnesses who had shared the experience were also talking about it.

A tiny apple fell just beyond my feet, its red shading reminding me of the rosy cheeks of a buxom barmaid. I listened for the "Hullo my luverly" but she said nothing.

Chapter Six

Feeling refreshed yet tired at the same time, I resisted the temptation of a Mediterranean style siesta, and instead got to my feet, turned and, hugging the big old grandmother tree, kissed her on her cheek and bid her farewell. No reply was given, just a friendly face as she watched me walk away.

I was happy; not wobbly leg excited, or award ceremony "wonderful darling" pleased, just happy. An inner peaceful happy, a subliminal happy.

I regarded the idea of leaving the place an insult after such an enlightening visit, where all the stops had been pulled out as if for my benefit. Surely all the messages and answers I had found were for me? It couldn't have been all coincidences could it? I refrained from adopting this idea as it would sour my now locked in illusion of pleasantness.

A key unlocked the padlock to my misguided mood quicker than I was ready for.

Along with a thought of "will it come off my shoe?", my 'Eco- friendly' facet put out the thought "is it alright?".

Looking down confirmed my fears, as there on the ground,

surrounded by the remains of his house around him, was a naked and helpless snail. He had the look on his face similar to that of a sad puppy with a bad case of diarrhoea. Not knowing whether to apologise or ask for help, not sure whether to direct the blame, or accept it.

I knew there was nothing I could do for him now. There were two choices.

One, I could accept the blame and see the crime right through to its fatal ending; after all, it would be only pleading guilty to a second crime, and have a second life sentence passed down on me, or, two, I could leave him to slowly die, abandoned to the vultures of semi-rural England, namely the starlings and rooks.

Rather than allow him to suffer any further indignity, I took my place as executioner. Hard-nosed and villainous with a Jimmy Cagney attitude, I brought down my right foot, and twisted it for good measure. I need not check my 'hit' for I knew in my mind that the deed was done.

I had intended to quietly walk away from the scene of crime, but remorse being the close relation of guilt, I felt obliged to stay and offer my condolences to the 'understanding' family. I tracked down their local address through the usual visual signs. Under the 'Cool and Damp Places', and 'Slimy Trails' sections of the snails yellow pages, I was given the details I required.

I thought a voice mail message would be rude, and a letter not personal enough, so I made my way to the address given.

Rolling back the large rectangular slab of stone, which weighed a good one hundred and thirty pounds, I felt as if I were opening their front garden gate. At their front door

I announced my arrival. After an initial period of silence, signs of movement became apparent.

I could not tell if I were addressing the mother, the father, the sister or the brother. To be honest, I tried to avoid eye contact as much as possible, so it was slightly awkward when it came to hearing a response. I did my best to explain the circumstances of the creatures untimely demise, tactfully omitting any gory details, and disguising the final ending, much to save my shame as much as their grief. After a suitable time I left them in the stunned silence, now either holding each other for support, or going off to a quiet spot to be alone for a while with their thoughts.

Feeling like a shamed schoolboy, I slowly, very slowly rolled the slab back over, allowing plenty of time in which any 'caught' shells could move out of the way in time, and thus have to go through the whole scenario again.

Walking short paced back down the mossy brick path, this shaded part of the garden seemed like a ghoulish forest, where spirits went to be forever tortured by their own displacement. The hedge at my shoulder seemed to be heckling me, while the long leafed plants at my feet were trying their best to nip at my heels.

The twigs of an overgrown shrub kept flying into my face and then pulling away at the last moment.

I could see the bright lime greened leaves of the hedge and bushes on the other side of this 'forest', where the bright sunshine was backlighting their playful dances. They had no shadows of dark against the light, just an invisible join where the shaded sides met the illuminated tops. The trees around them sparkled with reflected light like tiny wavelets on an emerald sea. The cloud formations had changed again and was now, that glorious combination of wonderfully white cumulus clouds with their beautifully defined curly edges set against a sky of infinite blues, from the softer, lighter blues, to the heavier more polarised deep blues. The sort of sky that could hold your gaze for hours, taking you on a fantasy journey up and around their fluffy tops, then down and through their glorious peaks and valleys. The kind of sky that you were happy to witness in celebration that mother nature ruled supreme.

First, I had to suffer, as is only right, the levelling and experience moulding process of being made responsible for my actions.

With the jeering crowd around me, the spirits of guilt prodded and pushed me, and after a telling period had elapsed, for I was sure the referee of fairness had deliberately added a period of extra time, the gatekeeper of forgiveness allowed me to pass, and there, in front of me, was a brighter, fresher, cleaner vista.

I entered the new arena cleansed of my crime, and was allowed immediately to resume my previous, if not microscopically adjusted, voyage of discovery and test of character.

My next encounter was strange to say the least, but then these things usually are.

Deciding it was pure coincidence, or a very sick joke on the part of 'Professor Deja Vu', I had selected an old upside down clay pot as worthy of my enquiring mind.

Its smaller end, currently on top, was about five inches in diameter, which made the wider open top, currently at the bottom, about twelve inches in diameter, with its height being approximately eighteen to twenty inches.

Owing to its size and weight, and the fact that its collared rim was held down by a paisley cravat of roots and uncut grasses, I placed both my hands around its base, still on the top, and pulled with a constant pressure until its cravat unfurled and allowed the pot to half- right itself. By completing the exercise and allowing it to show off its rightful shape, there inside, must have been a dozen snails, some in their shells, some poking their heads out, all randomly placed around the inside surface of the pot.

After deciding this meeting was pure coincidence, I started to see the funny side, and as I did, I was reminded of Bank Holiday Caravaners, all heading in the same direction, all with their own prepared route and destination, but, for now, all going round and round the same roundabout, or stuck in the same long traffic jam. Their drivers ranging from the Mr 'Stay in the car, I know what I'm doing', through Mrs 'Oh I don't know Dolly, I think that's what the sign said', on passed Mr 'I did check the oil and water before we left', who was now having to discreetly pee into his radiator to avoid overheating and consequent engine seizure, and through to Mr and Mrs 'Been there, done that', who had calmly unpacked the hamper, unfolded a pair of striped, metal framed chairs, and were contentedly sat at the side of the road, thermos in hand, white hats on heads, tinted shades at ninety degree angles to their spectacles, with the resigned patience of the British holiday maker.

Allowing the motorway madness to play itself out, I returned the pot to its upside down existence, and with it the chance of seeing the same tourists at the same time next year.

My mind, now having re-filed snails as 'slow moving

creatures, often found in cool parts of a garden, usually with integral shell', instead of 'easy targets for malicious murderers', was allowing itself the pleasure of choosing which areas of its complex database needed updating.

Corrugation, or rather, corrugated roofs was the next item on my muddled agenda. Looking up along the sloping sides of the curved wave pattern as it raised itself up to the apex of a nearby outbuildings roof, I wondered how it came about. Was it designed in some Victorian inventors front parlour, was it pioneered by an eccentric artist on one of his 'off' days, or did someone somewhere need a roof, and only had two dozen sheets to use up somewhere. Perhaps the benefit of the curves only came about after its use was discovered.

I can see the structural advantage of it, as the half-domes would greatly help its durability and strength. Its almost secondary function, that of allowing rainwater to run down and off it, would have been noticed around the time that the same person noticed how well the sheet edges overlapped each other and prevented any unwanted 'runback' of water under the joins.

Here again is a possible example of how waves came as a bonus to an otherwise ordinarily useful idea.

Maybe God had a hand in it again. Remember the oceans and the bonus of waves and surf? Perhaps God was playing some kind of universal celestial supermarket or garage forecourt points game, whereby you scratch off one panel to reveal a word, in this case, 'WAVE', and are then given nine other panels in which to choose three examples of the chosen word.

He already had the oceans and seas with their

accompanying waves as one example, the corrugated roofing gave him his second example, all that was left for him to do was to give a third example and he would scoop the prizes, these being the heavenly equivalent of a two week holiday in Florida, or a giant twenty four inch, flat screen, Dolby sound colour television.

If it were the holiday, he would have to go incognito, because although no-one would know what he looked like, hovering just above the sand on a beach towel, with cherubs playing harps all around, might raise suspicion or unwanted attention from the lifeguards.

If it were the television, he would certainly have the upper hand as far as satellite viewing went, but then would the system fit in with his decor?

I awaited this third and final prize winning example with a nonchalant interest.

Chapter Seven

Colonel Beech Log announced his presence. I acknowledged his salute and admired and congratulated him on his immaculately turned out troop of log soldiers, precisely and orderly arranged in their stacked formation. He informed me that he and his men were awaiting transportation, either on the ground by means of a transport vehicle, namely an armoured wheelbarrow, or, by air by means of human hands wrapped round them.

I suppose that must be where the phrase 'Brothers in arms' originates.

The 'DZ', or 'Drop Zone' would be just on the perimeter of the 'TZ', or Target Zone base. Some smaller units, probably outfits of the 'First Kindling and Newspaper Brigade' would go on ahead to set up a base and establish communications before the larger outfits of 'Stick and Log' Company would arrive ready to go in and 'Kick some Butt'. As a tactical diversion a branch unit would send up anti-aircraft flack into the skies above, while their comrades in the thick of it would literally turn the heat up.

In the dawn of a new day, the smoking battlefield would expose the mass destruction and losses suffered on both

Colonel Beech Log had that look about him, that suggested he knew it would be a one-way ticket, but he was prepared for this and proud to be doing it for the better of mankind. Not one man flinched as I stood there talking to Colonel Beech Log, a sign of true British training. I asked a couple of the men what they thought they would be facing, and if they felt ready for it. Aware that their Sergeant was listening in, they responded with appropriate comments.

Their Sergeant, a thick wristed, lean man had seen it all before. He had seen action in the previous winter when a paramilitary group known as the 'Freedom Fighters for Firework Night', or the '3FN' had threatened the peace that had reigned for years. He was sent in on a covert operation, named 'Flamingo', and was one of only three to survive. He received numerous burns to his body, some of which were still visible, but these were the only scars, either physical or mental, that he allowed to show.

I thanked them for their time, and, leaving them in their motorcycle display team formation, I allowed them to 'Stand Easy'.

I wondered if they would ever get to see action before their demob, or, if left in this inexperienced state, and not kept in peak condition, would they, the next time I saw them, be flabby, rusty and old.

Maybe they could leave the services and seek alternative employment. Security work, training camps for bored rich twigs, or, God help them, playing a combined role of host and instructor on one of those now all too common wastes of time known as Executive Leadership courses, which prove absolutely nothing and are just an excuse for some childish up and coming future Chairman, to prove to his chums what a total prat he or she could be.

The other, slightly less ridiculous trend nowadays is that of Corporate Hospitality, where a dozen or so misfits are put together, in either a boiling hot marquee and made to talk a load of empty and pointless conversations to people they are normally glad to see the back of, or, thrown onto a rolling and lurching vessel of nautical nature, favourite being sixty foot racing yachts, where they spend a day of being bruised, soaked and patronised by all around them, where seasickness is considered failure, and no one did their homework as regards to tides, destination, weather, or sizes of the crew, who now resemble space astronauts, dwarfed by their oilskins.

I don't know who to pity the most. The organisers who consider themselves creator of 'enlightenment', or the victims for not having the courage to say no to the late internal memo, requesting their presence at these 'occasions'.

I hope Colonel Beech Log and his fine stack of men never fall prey to such ordeals.

The thought glands in my head suffered an electrical surge and compelled the following notion into my cerebellum. I found myself considering whether or not there is a common link between pot plants, goldfish, light bulb filaments, hamsters and astronauts. They all live in a 'catch 22' lifestyle or situation. They are probably all fed up with being confined in their caged existences and restricted environments, and would love to roam freely in an open, unrestricted one, yet, at the same time, if they were to be taken out of their 'cells' and offered naked to this new world, they probably wouldn't exist for long.

The astronaut would go off drifting slowly, suffocating as he effortlessly glided out of orbit and into the black beyond, the hamster would constantly need a warm, dry, clean place, as well as food, and what would he have to play with except an old working water mills waterwheel, but this, being on the same ratio of Jack and the Giant at the top of the beanstalk, would mean unequalled feats of fitness and stamina, especially when you consider this would have to be done whilst in a drysuit, and there would always be the constant threat of colds, flu, then pneumonia and eventual death, drastically reducing his already short life span from four years to maybe only one candle on his birthday cake.

Goldfish, although resilient and easily adoptive of new surroundings, would have to begin sharing things, meeting other goldfish, being friendly when he or she didn't want to be, and above all, missing various soap operas, either on television, or in the house around him or her, while pot plants, the poor gentle things, would got into hysterical raptures at any surroundings other than the calm, warm and moist atmosphere they need for their own peace of mind. Like a hypochondriac on valium, our insecure friends would worry themselves to death long before any actual harm could come to them.

I left the light bulb filament to last because this needed thinking about. Apart from the obvious dangers and susceptibility towards injury that a naked uncased filament would risk, truer, more deep allowances and long term effects would have to be studied or experimented with.

My only thoughts on the matter, for now, centred around the mind of a filament, and how it, and its alien environment would co-exist. The now missing glass dome and the vanished chamber of neon gas would strip bare any protection that they had created, and, like a skinny child emerging from a cold sea, and being faced with a chilly breeze, our filament would shiver and feel totally exposed. How it would yearn the warm comforting wrappings of a big gaseous towel, how it would enjoy a hot mug of electricity, giving back a contented glow.

So, in surmise I concluded that although certain things seem sad, misplaced or unfair, the bigger picture and a comparison with stark alternatives gives us a moral to these examples and indeed to our own existence. It is better to be lonely and safe, than to never have experienced either. I couldn't refine it any further than that, but at least I had made an attempt, or, as we are driving through 'Quotation City', 'It is better to have tried and stumbled, than to never have tried at all'.

No doubt I would have eventually convinced myself of my psychoanalytical skills, but for now though, thoughts of an irritating pain kept reminding me that no one has yet designed a shoe in which a foot and stone can mutually agree on space allocation. This particular stone was fussing around trying to establish a point on the sole of my left foot, where it had the best bargaining power with its landlord.

Eventually, tenancy rights or no tenancy rights, this particular tenant would be sleeping rough tonight. In order to execute a swift and decisive eviction, I commandeered an appropriate seat nearby, namely Colonel Beech Log and his men, and sat down. I quickly undid the shoe lace and, without giving the occupant the time of day, I shook him out of his accommodation. I administered the usual courtesy rub to the affected part of my foot through my sock, before rehousing it in its quiet, private, low lit and slightly odorous apartment.

Chapter Eight

I was about to rise when out of an apparently empty sky above, there fell a particularly runny bird dropping, or 'guano' if we are to be polite, about six feet to my right. The sound it made on contact was similar to when an upset blancmange hits a floor of quarry tiles. It also had quite a respectable decibel rating. Maybe if I had not paused to evict the stone from my shoe I may have had a very organic shampoo on my head.

They say that to be hit by such a missile is considered lucky, so would I have been lucky to receive the airborne projectile, or lucky by not being hit? I left that one for the panel to decide.

When birds fly around, twisting, swooping, perching and circling high above, do they suffer from air sickness or nausea through imbalances in their mental horizons?

Hire a coach, invite a cross-section of the species, maybe two sparrows, four seagulls, three hawks, and, ever the optimist for their displeasure, half a dozen pigeons. Take them all up to Blackpool for a weekend at the fairground, wait for a generally over clouded, damp and cold day, and strap them all into their seats on the big roller coaster.

Leave them riding for say three goes on the trot and then ask each of them for their feelings and reactions. Hopefully the pigeons would be too sick and sore gulletted to respond, but the others might offer some interesting scientific data. Any found still in their seats, with both legs pointing straight up, could be considered too cocky for a rational response, or dead.

The 'slop' settled itself into its hardening shape as it enveloped a piece of gravel, and I resumed my walk back to the front of the garden.

Another old expression that one comes across from time to time is 'the older you get, the more keys you collect'. My makers must have misheard this one for I seemed to have collected many keys in my early days and shed various ones as I got older.

The set of four keys that were now in my front trouser pocket were a meagre showing for a lifestyle that had seen many 'locks' in its time.

The proverbial Yale lock key, a car key, one backdoor Chubb key and another old and hollow padlock or cash box type key that I had had all my life, yet never knew how I came to have it, or which lock it was for.

I didn't have the heart to throw it away, it would upset the balance of my key ring, it would be missed.

It was this key that I held between thumb and forefinger of my right hand as I pulled the set of keys out of my pocket. After confirming that yes, I did still have them with me, I returned the now warm metal objects and into my pocket and felt glad that I didn't have many keys. It helped keep things simple, not confused.

Somewhere in the distance there was music playing. I

couldn't be sure exactly what sort it was, but every now and then a few notes would be brought to me on a curl of wind as it lifted over the hedges. There was definitely a drum or baseline beat, a few electric guitar or keyboard rhythms, and either someone singing or a highly strung instrument.

On one hand I enjoyed the mysterious collection of sounds, while on the other hand I felt that it clashed with the images and sounds immediately around me. I felt as if it would be a betrayal to allow the tune to merge with the local scene. The matter was soon decided, as either a car door was shut, thus containing the music in its falsely secure, electronically monitored cell of comfort, a group of budding musical icons were warming up for a gig, or, the more plausible of the three options, someone turned their radio off.

I had reached a part of both time and place where I could not venture further, and rather than try and push down the side panel fencing with my nose, I turned around and started to retrace my steps.

Every few steps I would take on the appearance of someone suffering from a Compulsive Obsession Disorder, COD for short, and found myself stopping, backtracking one or two paces, and having just one more look at this, or just confirming the position of that, slowly convincing myself I had the complete measure of the place.

That was, until, while slowly assessing one dimension, I spotted a nicely rounded pebble, about one inch in diameter, laying invitingly on the path before me.

Now what it is about stones on pathways that seem to trigger a response in us humans, namely a desire to become one of our footballing heroes and pass, chip, or simply blast the 'ball' into the back of the net.

Quickly selecting a piece of tree trunk about twenty yards in front of me, I aimed, distributed my body weight for ultimate effectiveness, and moved in on the pebble, whilst judging the distance and my pace, to allow my left foot to fall neatly to the side of the pebble, which would allow my right foot to make contact with maximum force.

I didn't feel the pebble on the toe of my shoe as my lower leg swung on its hip and knee pendulous movement, nor the satisfying clicky sound that acknowledges a cracking strike. Looking down at my feet, the pebble seemed to still be in its 'ready to fire canon pose', tensed and prepared for imminent launch, so I felt duty bound to quickly administer a back up shot.

Swiftly bending my right leg at the knee joint and raising my lower right leg, I threw my arms out sideways, not knowing why, but allowing the automated movement to flow through, before bringing my right foot down in a kind of stabbing, digging and punchy manner.

The pebble took off and shot dead ahead with remarkable force as it skimmed many flower heads, before dropping not on target, but down out of sight behind a mixed bunch of osteospurnums and lavender.

I thought I would never discover the pebble's fate, but as it landed it gave out a metallic rattling sound, similar to the sound you hear after 'all bets' have been placed at the roulette wheel, and the white ball slows on its 'wall of death' ride, and skips and bounces around the rim and the numbered grooves in the spinning wheel. This was then followed by the sound achieved when dropping large ice cubes into a tall jug of lemon squash.

My curiosity again stepped in, and ushered me down and sideways across the border until I was virtually on top of, and could only just make out a drain, or more precisely, a drain grill. Not your DIY superstore 'cheap at the weekend' type of grill, but a heavy traditional, durable fellow. The type that was once made in a local foundry, where twenty or so men would each heartily contribute a small portion of its creation. I couldn't make out any name on it, but I didn't need to know the company, the mens efforts rubber stamped its qualities.

Unfortunately, the once proud grill had become entangled with twigs, root systems and long grasses, with a splattering of rotten last year's leaves, dead flower heads and general garden refuse, which had masked the grill in grotesque features, now making it resemble a street urchin from the seventeenth century, whose grime and boil covered face would only change colour by being covered with the latest offering of food or drink or worse.

Like a Quasimodo of the drainage world, it had accepted its fate, and although he yearned to be a handsome overflow and marry his Esmarellda downpipe, he had been denied these pleasures.

In a bid to rewrite certain events and stories, I cleared away the leaves, pulled out the roots and wrapped my fingers under its bars and pulled it upwards and free. Down below in its chamber of nasties, there were numerous foreign objects that had no right being there, indeed I wondered how they got there in the first place.

In for a penny and all that, I rolled up my right arm shirt sleeve and, gaining enthusiasm for my quest, knelt down and leaned over the surface, and steadying my weight with my left hand on the far edge, plunged my right hand down into the dark muddy soup, and started to explore with my fingers, the many different shapes and textures that were hidden.

I found something long and solid but slippery and decided that this was to be the first object to be extracted, before re-plunging my arm into the now slightly odorous mixture and seeking other 'things' from the depths to follow it.

The chamber itself was probably no more than eighteen inches deep, by two feet wide and three feet long. I was confident of my estimate of its depth as now, my right arm was covered with an eighteen inch long, browny black glove of silt.

My fingers had probed the bottom two inches of mud and other slime, before finding a surprisingly smooth surface at the bottom of the chamber.

I slowly worked my way through the sloppy mess, either swooshing the smaller fragments on down the next stage of the pipe work, or bringing out the larger pieces of wood, stone, brick, and a fibrous object about the size of an orange, which, on closer inspection, revealed itself to be an old split tennis ball.

The remaining slurry I left behind, partly because of its now rather pungent, 'rotting' smell, but mainly because it simply kept running through my fingers every time I tried to retrieve some.

All around the drain hole was a browny grey collar of ooze, with a sprinkling of the larger objects recovered. The now revived grill was slowly lowered back into place, where I left it, ready to face the season's new crop of debris.

Who knows, maybe he actually now had a chance with Esmarellda.

My immediate problem was my right arm which, now covered in its non-beauty treatment, was beginning to dry and urgently required rinsing off.

I began to regret my spontaneous efforts to rejuvenate Quasimodo, and started looking for a suitable water container, still holding its contents. Luckily, just inside the foreground of the border next to me was a rusty circular tin, roughly the size of a five litre paint tin, which still held some of the rain from a recent downpour. Being careful not to disturb the bottom contents inside the tin, I lowered my right hand into the fresh clean water, while using my left hand as a scoop, to throw the water up onto my right elbow and above.

After a few delft rubs and rinses my arm was practically its normal shade of flesh, and, unrolling my sleeves back down onto still wet skin, I felt cleansed of any incriminating evidence of my involvement with the drain. Next to the rusty old tin were two lolly sticks, crossed over each other, forming an 'X' where they lay. Perhaps they had been placed there as a marker for an insect team involved in a search and rescue mission. Any time now a squadron of bumble bees, loaded up with supplies, vitamins, and a medical kit, would fly in low, and release their cargo, to the relief of the stranded party on the ground. Maybe whoever it was, had been there for days, weeks or months. Maybe they were survivors of a horrific mid air crash involving three bees, two bluebottles, and a mosquito, who were now trying to get on with each other, resisting the temptation of cannibalism, and just waiting and hoping to be saved.

Now weakened by a lack of diet, and exercise to their flying muscles, they would be weak, their wings would be cracked and torn. I wondered if the male survivors would all have long beards by now and if everyone was walking around in some hallucinogenic trance.

Then again, maybe the lolly sticks had just simply fallen in that position.

Chapter Nine

If Autumn is the time in the natural world when everything is prepared, dates noted, and seeds sown, so as to reward the parents with new offspring the next year, then springtime is the time of reward, time of plenty, time for new life to be born.

All birds would be tending to nests, searching the local area for a suitable residence. Maybe they have their own version of estate agents, with characters such as 'Robin' from the company 'Swan, Gull and Robin, Your Local Housing Experts'. Each knowledgeable of a certain type of habitat. Mr Swan on river frontage properties, Mr Gull on seaside apartments, and our Mr Robin, the king of the urban scene.

Every morning around five thirty, he would fly along to the head office where sales leads and appointments have been set up for him by their secretary Miss Olivia Kingfisher, the day before. Then, off he would fly to his first morning's appointment, a Mr and Mrs Bluetit, looking for a comfortable springtime abode.

At the appointed time our Mr Robin would be stood on the roof of the birdhouse, casually kicking stones while he waits. Then a few minutes later, the couple arrive, anxious and excited, trying not to look too keen and staying calm and business like.

After a brief guided tour, our Mr Robin leaves Robert and Mary Bluetit to go round, in and out, on their own. Both seemed pleased with their 'find' and, unlike humans, where an offer is made, followed by a tussle of phone calls, reoffers, surveys and quotations, our Mr and Mrs Bluetit simply nod to each other, call over Mr Robin who raises and twists his head from side to side, followed by Mr and Mrs Bluetit nodding at Mr Robin,who finally agrees and, raising and lowering his tail feathers, seals the deal.

As it was vacant possession, Mary and Robert begin at once, clearing out any old grubs, pieces of dirt, spiders webs etc., and then, while Mary gives it the floor a final 'once over', Robert goes off to the local salvage yards, DIY Superstores and antique shops, collecting twigs for the base of the interior, grasses and leaves for the middle sections of carpet, before choosing bits of cotton wool, dog hair, foam, and other such insulating fabric for the soft furnishings.

This process, when done well, normally takes a good week, by the end of which time, Mary Bluetit, who chose a home birth is restricted to light duties and only flights that are essential.

Finally the big day would arrive, and Mary, who had plumped for a drug free delivery, would now bear the pain, awkwardness and totally tiring business of egg birth.

No drink down the pub with his mates, or cigars 3, or nearest tree, where, with head held high and proud breast pushed out, he would sing out to his neighbours the good news.

I felt the need to leave soon, as well as to explore just a little longer. Why had this place captivated me, and allowed me to be enveloped by its hugging arms. Was it this place that needed me, or was it me that needed this place, and why?

I was pondering this conundrum, as I realised I was using a fencing panel as a sounding board. I kept studying its interlocking pieces and the woven textures of its thin slices of planking. My hand, in the same way you admire an antique, felt the need to touch it, to move your fingertips across its surface, to absorb its character through your skin. Its raised grain following the cut of the band saw like some weed pointing downstream while its shape and the flow of the water push it one way then the other.

It felt familiar, normal, not obvious. The way we assume the person driving a milk float is really a milkman, or the who says he is our doctor, really has trained in medicine, and not aircraft technology.

Isn't it funny how we as humans need constant reassurance that we are in tune with ourselves, have control, think we know how to balance things.

We kit ourselves out with what we consider a 'suitable' environment, not too radical, not too stayed, an appropriate amount of naturalism, and just enough comfort to prevent guilt marring the 'ideal'.

We have been on this planet for less than a wing beat of time, yet we feel so in control, so self satisfied, and if anything comes into view to irritate or jolt our perspective of things, we again create an excuse or a 'realism', and lay a mattress of uncertainty over the barbs of actual events.

A parallel, though more basic comparison is when you're driving your car, and you pass a cyclist, on what to you seems a slight incline, on a fairly bright day, going at a gentle cruising speed of say forty miles an hour, in your comfortable though not luxurious, quiet though not silent, powerful but not racey motor car.

Its only when you change places with the cyclist, that you realise, in real time and space, the incline is a hill, the bright day is cold, and the unnatural speed of driving has all but eradicated your awareness of speed. Your ears have forgotten all the sounds that can be heard, instead of the one that they are forced to listen too.

One answer might be to develop a house with the kitchen outside. Unwanted peelings and stale bread could simply be scattered around, encouraging local wildlife, and saving the need for a trendy wormery. Washing up would be more a case of raining down, and to top it all, no need to buy an expensive 'real wood' set of units that have 'raised grain effect' for a natural feel.

I thanked the fence panel for this insight. Patent Pending. The hot sun was going onto full beam, and like a terrestrial rabbit, I was caught in its gaze. The warm bricks around me in this corner of the garden wall were radiating a further heat, which combined with the warm breeze, made for an efficient fan assisted oven effect.

Why do we never see or hear of any plants suffering from sunburn, or for that matter, at the other end of the scale, frostbite. No discarded suntan lotion bottles, or thermal socks and gloves for them, so how do they achieve this all year round control of skin moisture and heat?

I was ready to assume, quite rationally, that mother nature, being the greatest dispensing chemist there is, had implanted these ingredients either physically or, over a long period of time, and through years of evolution, subliminally, somewhere where we could solve the puzzle if we were to beat to a different drum of awareness. Not the kind that would have us seeing fairies knitting gloves and scarfs, or elves mixing cool drinks and rubbing copious quantities of calamine lotion into the roots, but, a more advanced yet simpler, clearer set of rules.

Some believe in fairies and elves, some would like to, and some will never believe, but who is right? I'll leave that one to the trees.

Trees played a disjointed stepping stone as my mind was drawn from a philosophical train of thought, to an observational few moments.

At the back of next doors; by the way, there's another of those funny quips we have kept, 'next door'. I wondered if one day, in a sleepy hamlet somewhere, there were two identical front doors side by side, and because he was knew to the job, the local postman went to put an envelope through one of the doors, when, with a start the door swung open and a grumpy unshaven, round bellied occupant snatched the envelope, studied the address, and then, with bubbling annoyance, said, as if he had said it many times, "you want the next door".

Gradually over time the words "you want the", would have dropped away, for economy sake, so that we are left with just the words "next door", and now instead of just one part of the house, we label the whole building, garden, plot, even farm or county, as, "next door".

As I was saying, at the back of 'next door's garden, a tall

row of pendulous conifer trees were forming into a hedge, pushing their heads up higher and higher. Looking at their tops, as they swung to and fro, their silhouettes against a crisp white set of clouds, reminded me of charging medieval knights with banners and pennants flying on the breeze, or, more humorously, witches at altitude, scaling the hedgerows and church roofs in search of vital ingredients for a brew, or on their way to a coven version of a WI meeting. Not much business for a Tupperware rep, and as for an Anne Summers party, well, it doesn't bear thinking about.

To rid my mind and mouth of such a sour image, I looked for something, anything, to freshen my mud stained thoughts.

My fabric softener in this particular wash, was a pair of tall, satin red Californian poppies, their petals shimmering in the light as their contours and smooth sides moved from side to side.

The image was soon dispersed, as there in between these elegant, charming creatures, was an empty crisp packet.

Suddenly I was watching a cheap television quiz show, and there between the slender models was an unwanted, crinkled up and faded form of a 'celebrity', trying, though not succeeding, to have us believe that this incompatible mixture is what we want, or worse still, need, to see.

I did the girls, and the country a favour, picked up the 'celebrity' crisp bag, crunched it up in my hand and gave it a ride, not in a swanky limousine, but a more suited vehicle, namely my jacket pocket, to not the expected green room of hospitality, but the next rubbish bin I found.

Chapter Ten

When I look at trees I always have a feeling of respect, of welcome, curiosity. When I am amongst trees I feel like a favoured guest, always allowed to study them up close, investigate the ground they stand in. Many a time I have been allowed to lay on the floor on my back and, like a pageboy at a wedding reception, look up the various dresses at the different undergarments that are to be seen. Today though I was studying the forms of many different trees, as I scrutinised the small wood next to the field, behind the house.

They say that dog owners eventually take on a resemblance to their dogs. Well, in this case, as I looked at each one in detail, I was reminded of a human 'type' rather than individual people.

Directly at the front of the wood was an old Oak. Strong, silent, experiencing the four seasons, year after year, like maybe a Dales farmer, or a west country herdsman. No immediate good looks or charm, but an awareness that under the weather beaten skin, there was strength, durability and experience.

Behind the Oak, a Chestnut. Don't ask me why, but

resembling a city gentleman preparing for the seasons social calendar. Neatly presented trunk, with a fine cut of cloth on him. The green leaves of his charm starting to flourish as he announces himself to his neighbours.

In contrast, and to my left and his right, predictably near the stream, was the old hippy, the Weeping Willow. Long strangely locks of branches swaying easily with the winds tune, feeling 'at peace man' with all around him.

I need not remind you of our Beech family, whose shoulders back, upright poise, always reflect the discipline of their forefathers.

Why I don't like Holly trees I don't honestly know. They give us decorations at Christmas, they afford good anti-burglar protection around a house, and the berries do look nice, especially on a variegated specimen. Maybe it's their prickly exterior, this 'not listening to reason' attitude they give out, that doesn't earn them my favour. For now, I'll put them in the category of a Doctors surgery receptionist. Pointed, obtuse and full of their own self importance.

Looking over next door, I can just make out a Cherry tree who, after having applied her blusher and eyeliner, is putting on a floral dress, ready for another night of pubs and clubs. I call her Sandra for no other reason than it came into my head. I can see her now, sitting on a high barstool, with roots crossed, her lower branches and slimmer higher ones dipping and rocking to the beat of the sound system, while her top twigs sip from an umbrella clad glass of turquoise and pink sap juice.

A few smaller trees, a dwarf maple, a small fir, and a chestnut sapling, saunter up to her and make what they think is 'cool' conversation. Our streetwise Sandra dismisses them all without saying a word, before suddenly, she sees her ideal Bo.

Entering the club is Geoff, a big powerful specimen of a Copper Beech. He acknowledges our Sandra, and before her mate Rhododendron can bring over a tray with the next round of drinks, she nudges up to his manly trunk, and remains there for the remainder of the evening.

Rhododendron Rachel faces another night of sipping alone, and the usual 'getting off' with one of Sandra's rejects. But no, whose this? Rachel's eyes widen, her mouth slightly parts. As if from a romantic novel, a gorgeous young Beech, who obviously works out, is making a path to her. He gazes down at her, she gazes up at him, and without words, their branches entwine, both having been struck by Cupids arrows.

For reasons of decency, we leave both our happy couples to their woody world of love.

On Sunday morning, our next tree, we'll call him 'Big V', will be polishing his sermon ready for delivery to his amassed followers. Tall and lean, our religious Poplar tree will don his cassock of service, and talk 'poker faced' to his flock, before inviting the ladies of the Laurel Hedge Sewing committee, around for a quick sherry and chat regarding their efforts to duplicate a medieval tapestry.

Young and effervescent, our charming Vicar swoons the ladies, and without exception, gets a vote of confidence for whatever cause is to be addressed.

Why, Cynthia Clematis was once seen up a ladder, sponging off the church clock face, at six o'clock in the morning. Now there's dedication!

Now, in the late afternoon, I allowed to surface, a hitherto suppressed realisation that it was time to quickly summarise what I had seen and thought here, see if any conclusions could, or should be reached.

I rewound my memory bank and replayed my minds tape. There wasn't the time to digest, assess and debate subjects now, I would need time to find and admit certain realities that would be reached, through the unrealities I had created. Where I would need to be to achieve this, I didn't know, I knew it couldn't be here and I knew it wouldn't be now.

I cut the chord of data collection and made that vital step through the gateway, before half looking back and closing the wooden gate behind me.

As I walked away, I didn't look behind me, instead, I tapped my top shirt pocket, where the drawing pin was, and then, raising my right arm above my head whilst leaving the scene, helped God towards his third and prize-winning goal, by giving him another example of the word 'WAVE'.

Chapter Eleven

I have many types of walk that I can call upon to suit the many situations I find myself in. There's the confident 'I don't know where I'm going but at least I look like I do' walk, which is good for larger towns and odd visits to London.

There's the 'functional strut' which is used when posting letters, buying bread and milk, or running general errands around town. My preferred natural style is the slower 'beach pace' which I use for watching waves, looking out to sea, or just relaxing and enjoying myself.

The 'functional' walk, I use at weddings, funerals, and other social occasions, usually accompanied by the crossing of hands, in front of, or behind one's back.

Today it was another, the 'gentle stroll', similar to a tourist's amble, but with slightly more purpose, and less picture taking.

Walking down the high street I looked across the road to the row of obedient cars, all sat there, one behind the other, waiting for their masters to come back and. Some having been turned around, were now sniffing each other's bumpers and exercise them making mental notes of each others breeds, class and other personal tags.

Some were working animals, some, more general breeds, and some just simply 'show specimens', brought into town twice a week by their owners to remind everyone of their prowess. I gauged two people might be interested.

The single yellow line which escorted the kerb as it veered round the corner in front of me, detected my presence, and with a gesture, welcomed me to join in, as like any enthusiastic tour guide, it started passing historic house after historic tree, after historic public house.

I could have allowed myself to join the package deal wanderer, but I like the independent, backpacking method of starting here, going there, having to get there, and ending up somewhere else. Much more fun.

As I rounded one corner, another predictable urban sight came into view. Sat, or stood under the half enclosed bus shelter were the usual collection of disheartened young mothers with heavy bags of shopping, patient pensioners who long ago, had accepted the waiting stage of public transport. A couple of likely lads sporting the latest gel look in their hair, and wearing a collection of 'in' clothes. Then there is always a single, business type woman in these corralled commuter stations. Maybe a secretary, maybe a director, maybe off to an interview, but always with a sensible shoulder bag, jacket and skirt, and usually accompanied by the personal assistant in the form of a mobile phone.

Everyone has that distant, protective gaze on their faces, like that of a line court judge at a tennis match, only to be open to different facial expression once prompted by a third party.

Eventually, as if by instinct, everyone goes on standby a split second before their chariot grudgingly comes round a bend and, as if doing them a favour, pulls halfway into its designated stopping area, and always, as if in spite, stops the opposite end of the glass wall of the shelter to the end where its future occupants are queued.

Single decker buses I can live with, economically viable, usually clean and not unnecessarily a burden to environment or road surface.

Unlike, their larger, smellier and more dangerous namesakes, the double decker.

It has an attitude all of its own. Okay for big cities where big attitudes are all part of the survival ritual, but not for smaller towns.

It's like seeing a Hollywood star pop into a small town hairdressers. Neither party sure of the outcome and both totally uneasy. Imagine the conversation;

Hairdresser: "Going away anywhere this summer?"

Star: "Oh, only New York, Hawaii and Monaco."

Hairdresser: "Oh really? Well aren't we the lucky one."

Star: "Yes, so get on with it!"

Hairdresser: (now annoyed) "Well excuse me, Miss sleep with the producer and now I'm famous, whoops there go my knickers again."

The following scene of flying plastic capes, pointed scissors, and torn tights, is only upstaged by the falling strands of ripped out hair, and multiple wrestling moves that would do credit to Hulk Hogan. Flying combs, jars of gel smeared into faces, head and arm locks are all ensued by alternate bouts of rodeo style bronco riding that are now performed.

No, double decker buses have, for me, one place and one place only - museums.

The bus shelter was doing its best to be chic and suited to its surroundings, but like some of the shop fronts and their facia boards, it should have been updated long ago.

Now and then cyclists would go by. Some on a quest to get fit, or because they're late, some gently ambling along in their own little world. The slower ones resemble everyone from your Uncle Bob, through the keen British cycling enthusiast, and on to the lost foreign visitor in their bright garish colours.

The faster ones are indicative of either the puffing businessman, hoping that he can stop breathing so fast in time to appear human at his next meeting, or, the speedy racer who, with elbows bent and legs going like pistons, appears as if he has made contact with a melon that fell off some lorry, and is now sporting a lime green dome on top of his head.

In the middle of the pavement stands a one legged litter bin, looking like a ballerina who, in mid pirouette, had been blasted with liquid nitrogen, and frozen in time and movement. Not realising that they had such an enchanting performer beneath their fingertips, people were dropping litter in or around her, so that instead of being cheered with lilies and red roses, our supreme ballerina was suffering the humiliarity of empty chip bags and bubble gum wrappers.

This time of year another softening effect takes place, and gives a so called warm friendly feel to the buildings such as banks, hotels, solicitors and shops.

This yearly decorating takes form in the shape of hanging baskets that, as if overnight, have been hung out on their brackets, to sweeten and colour a normally empty and colourless airspace.

To me, they remind me of criminals. Not the white collar variety, or your average Bank robber, but the lower, more guttural type, slimy and rotten. The kind that appears in Carry On films covered in manure and straw, munching away with open blackened teeth and sideways moving jaw, dribbling as much as he consumes.

These social outcasts have been strung up in their moss ridden cages, in full view of the chuckling public, made to look like the fools they are and, to add insult to injury, or maybe just to keep the smell down, there comes along their jailer who, with pole and long hose of torture, hoses them down twice a day.

The only evidence of this treatment being a temporary puddle beneath them on the pavement, and a sorrowful, but again temporary, limpness to their appearance.

Their sentence is a seasonal one, when around October time, or sometimes later, they are spared the freezing of winter whilst still airborne, and released.

Not to some warm propagating shed or poly tunnel, but simply turfed out onto a larger heap of rotting matter, and left to fend for themselves, or, recycled into more socially acceptable organic compost.

Chapter Twelve

I could tell I was getting near the busiest part of the town by the increasing numbers of street lights. These tall, thin, trifid like beings seem so duty bound and static. Like a ship full of slaves rowing their Emperor across the sea, they perform their task when required to do so, and then, left there in the same spot until required again. If any fail, or don't give one hundred percent performance, the rhythm drummer continues, while the sad, now worn out being is taken away and immediately replaced by another faceless creature.

Sometimes, the Emperor's rowing chief, namely the council lighting department, don't notice a failure straight away, and our lackless soul is left, side by side with his compatriots, his body moving whilst still clung to the oar, but contributing nothing to the fast, smooth pace of illumination.

Maybe, every once in a while, a courageous Charleton Heston type mortal will challenge his role in life, and by guts and guile, break free from his chains of capture and rise against his oppressors.

Now not shining simply downward, our gathering mass

of mutineers would stride up the high street, swinging their bulbous heads from side to side, and even upwards, towards the heavens, celebrating their rightful freedom. Some may bend down and kiss the tarmac, others would just be caught up in the ecstatic emotions of the hour.

Some, more reclusive or paranoid specimens would seek a forest of tall pine trees, and, relishing in their new hermit like existence, hide away in their new found paradise, out of the gaze of possible trackers.

Our Emperor, the great Borough Council, would be left without permanent lighting around his kingdom. Okay, a few neon signs, traffic lights and car headlamps would offer some, if not a pitiful, amount of relief, but he would have to totally regroup and assess what to do.

After sacrificing a few scapegoats such as town council, environment and leisure and a chief executive or two, he would then have to be advised by his now chief of staff, the Technical Division.

Soon, propane fired lamps would be scattered like grass seeds, all across the darkened land, giving the country an appearance of Cinderella's Castle by nightfall. Then, while waiting for further instructions, our now disillusioned workforce would plead treble time for such unsociable hours, causing the council coffers to rapidly empty, thus causing a viscous circle of expenditure, workload, panic, expenditure, and so on.

National demand for alternative lighting sources would soar and the stock market would send shares in candle wax shooting skywards.

Our now lonely Emperor Borough Council would last be seen walking, with dimming torch in hand, quietly sobbing and softly shaking, towards the coast of West Sussex and its prominent cliffs of Beachy Head, where a few days later, the smashed and rotten corpse would be discovered at their base.

At these thoughts, I instantly warmed to our metallic, stick like friends, and as I passed the first of them, I offered my support for their cause, and, like a fellow mutineer, greeted him, by tapping the palm of my hand a couple of times on the upright curved surface of its base.

Similar things come in many guises. All it takes is to hold off the usual reactionary thought and assessment, and look for a more lateral idea.

An example is garage forecourts. To many people they are simply garage forecourts, but to me, well, I can see the similarity between the garage forecourt and a brothel. Not some high class escort agency where postcodes and vintages are all part of the attraction, but more of your down to earth city centre example.

Both have welcoming illuminated signs, with maybe a few colourful bits hanging from suspended wires.

They fulfil a need, by satisfying a thirst and are only really used at time of necessity, although a few regulars patronise the establishments no matter how full their tanks are.

You arrive, enter and take in the many basic offerings as well as a few extras that await the slightly more adventurous client. You move into the central part, or, wait in line for your turn at particularly busy times, usually Friday and Saturday nights, unless a coach load of Japanese businessmen happen to drop in, in which case, profit comes before customer satisfaction. Eventually you select or enquire about a selection. Do you go for high spirited Fiona four star, a favourite of many, the more basic Lucy unleaded who has more staying power, or maybe the delectable Debbie diesel, economical and not prone to overheating your engine.

For the more 'selective' client, a further array of more 'specialised' products are available in the shop part of the business, where all tastes are catered for.

Cheap tacky plastic accessories, oils and waxes for the more orientally persuaded, quality items for the travelling executive, or rubber items for 'home' use only.

After one feels fulfilled and satisfied, and after, if needs be, they've washed their hands and brushed their hair, he or she concludes the business side of things by paying the 'Madame', or the male equivalent, at the cash desk, usually whilst being watched by another figure stood behind the counter, close by.

Then it's simply a matter of returning to your car, van etc., or merely walking out, and, leaving the facility behind, disappearing into the day or night.

I wonder if brothels give Tiger Tokens?

Not so much the noise, but more the smell greeted me as I turned left off the high street. I say greeted because the smell was an old friend. Unmistakable, unique and yet widespread.

As the lorry slowly arched its back and the semi molten tarmac and stone mixture slid slowly off the edge of the lorry, two men were helping it along by raking it out in smaller portions. The two men behind them were raking the now fallen mixture evenly across the next stretch of prepared road, before another man, riding high on a life sized Dinky toy road roller, was going backwards and forwards over the same piece of freshly laid surface. As its wetted wheels left behind the finished article, a steady but gently curtain of wriggling steam rose off the road and one could sense the tarmac relaxing after its ordeal.

Like a well trained army of Japanese soldiers reaching their objective of their mission, I saw them as not resting, but stood to attention in honour of their belief in their cause. They would have all begun at a stone quarry 'Bootcamp', where specimens from many regions would be crammed together for initial inspection. Some would receive more 'discipline' than others, but eventually all would be knocked into shape, so that they were ready for transportation to their first posting. A roadside depot, or a government holding stockyard. These were the lucky ones. The more unfortunate ones would be sent out on emergency missions, where although proficient in basic skills, they would not be prepared for the shame and the peril of such places as farm gateways, annual trade shows or, worst of all, reclamation of bogs and marshes, where unseen, they would unwittingly contribute to the 'progress' of urban sprawl.

We must not forget too, those courageous and perfectly able souls, who, having made it through all the 'shaping' courses and training courses put upon them, are subject to that most heartless of outcomes, the let down of, 'being surplus to requirements'.

These undeserving men, and I suppose women, are simply moved aside and crushed, washed, some even coloured for goodness sake, and left with barely two options, both totally inappropriate and insulting. They are given the choice of becoming 'Anti Skid' grit, where they are simply sprayed across freezing cold and watery ice and snow, in the hope of preventing some poor human from denting his new Mercedes, then left to disappear into the hedges, drains, or muddy banks along the sides of the road, never to be seen again, or, option two, and this to me seems insulting, even perverse, they are steam-cleaned, sterilised, and dyed numerous citrus colours, before being placed, in full view of the ogling public, at the bottom of fish tanks to help co-ordinate Gordon the Guppy's interior which consists of sunken treasure chest, plastic bridge and sunken submarine! The whole ensemble resembling an exploded paint box that some misguided owner considers 'Tres Chic'.

Gordon the Guppy would have been placed there against his will, but at least he can move around, changing his now psychedelic view from 'lemon yellow' to 'cobalt blue' and onto 'lime green', and, if feeling particularly aggrieved at his surroundings, can either go on hunger strike, or deposit his disapproval in the unconvincing treasure chest.

The lucky successful candidates of our special forces army continue their training and exercises, going through mock up attacks and gathering information in readiness for the big assault.

Finally the day comes and, kitted up, psyched up, and their faces blacked up, our army of tough and knowledgeable young men and women board their final transporter lorry. As the 'DZ' (Drop Zone) approaches, final thoughts of home, and humorous banter diminish, to leave an earthly silence.

Then, with a jolt as the lorry brakes to a stop, their minds switch to trained autopilot. The rush of the air brake as it clamps onto the wheel pre-empts the louder, more grating screech, as the vehicle arches its back and the whole regiment begin to slide down an ever increasing metallic slope.

Not stampeding, or rushing over one another, but in ordered, disciplined movements, the first wave reach the drop off edge. Here there is no panic, no fear, just another part of a well rehearsed routine.

They leave the edge, and after flying unsuspended through the air, they land as expected, in uniformed rows on the ground.

No time for regrouping or damage assessment, for they have to be in position within the allotted time of 3.4 seconds, before the sympathetic resistance workers of the human underground, arrange them in their final 'dug in' positions.

Once in place they can afford a final check for missing buttons, torn shirts or slipped caps. Finally, with great relief, the air cover arrives and as it deals with any rebel pieces of rock, it clears the surroundings of unwanted 'annoyances', before pushing our men into secure and comfortable bitumen foxholes, where, with rigorous and highly effective deterrent, they stand the test of time with pride and honour.

Chapter Thirteen

The sky today was reflective of the kerb stones along the side of the street. Trying its best to dry out and brighten up, but being covered by unwanted water every now and then, making a greyish stone shaded blanket of colour.

Birds have the advantage here because any time they want a bit of sunshine on their backs, they simply fly up through the cloud-base and into clear skies and warm, uninterrupted sunshine. If the cloud is too thick or high to prevent such a nicety, our feathered friends simply go to roost, or go for a stroll in the woods, stocking up on basics such as worms for vitamins, slugs for carbohydrates and grit based moss and lichen for roughage. Even birds need to be regular!

Our only hoping of glimpsing the sun on such a day is to develop a new danger sport, the opposite of Bungee jumping, let's call it 'Ekasterocket', where from any point on the ground, you could be propelled up to a height of say three and a half thousand feet, where for a brief moment, you can be reminded of the warmth and cheeriness of the suns rays. This cheeriness would be short lived, as the realisation of gravity would take over and unless your parachute opened as required, you would plummet earthwards, with little chance of ever seeing the sun again. Failing this idea, rob many banks so you can afford various long hauled flights, and enjoy the aforementioned attractions from the comfort of a 747.

Nearing the popular town centre, all the 'encouraging' signals are there to be latched onto. The pub sign, offering two bar meals for the price of five pounds, when eaten between the hours of 3pm and 4pm on Monday, Tuesday, or Wednesday, and as long as it is from the pub menu and eaten in the saloon bar where no jeans are allowed, but children can be accompanied by parents, and that coffee would be extra. Much simpler to have a pint and a packet of cheese and onion.

The gift shops that offer things to remind you of your stay, like gilt edged Polar bears, or white china Koala bears, a wooden snake or a silver-plated cup with the inscription 'Mine's Earl Grey' on the side. Okay if your name is Earl Grey, but lesser mortals have to make do with 'She's the Boss' or 'Deckchair attendants have you lying back all day!'.

My favourite attraction has to be the toy shops, either disguised as a newsagent, or in full blown 'Buy It Here' fashion. Maybe because they feature so much in my own childhood that they seem so ageless, so unchanged, so enjoyable to look around. The childish packets of practical jokes, from itching powder to 'nail through the finger', the colourful selection of buckets and spades in their blues, yellows, reds and greens. The inflatable rings, boats, armbands all vacuum packed in their plastic bags. Rows of jellyshoes, plimsoles and flip flops, water pistols, postcards, sun creams, hats, wind breakers, beach mats, flags and, for some uncanny reason, always boxes of fudge. I reminded myself of a suspicion that until now, I had forgotten about. Outside the shop, standing like arthritic flowers, and spinning randomly, depending on strength and direction of whatever breeze was blowing, were the ever popular windmill stars on sticks. The metallic backed ones reflecting the sun like some Morse code trainee with flashlight in hand, while the more primary coloured ones simply spun and spun, like some bored animal trapped in its confines.

Most people think that this is all they are, toys to be enjoyed from being held in the hand or stuck on top a sandcastle, or pushed into a lawn in the garden.

We all think that wind vanes and high powered wind turbines are a recent development, and that the fields of Kent enjoy a ground breaking technological system of supplying power to the masses.

Who's to say that this modern approach wasn't actually highjacked many generations ago, say when gas lamps were all the rage, by some government agency looking for alternative power supplies, and that they couldn't publicise their findings until recently because Joe Public and society at that time didn't have the appropriate infrastructure to accommodate it.

Now, if this is the case, where was the idea highjacked from? My theory is this.

At the base of each and every plastic or wooden windmill there is some, as yet unknown by us, secret power transmitting quality and this converts the wind power into a manageable energy which is transmitted through its base and into whatever receptors are available.

Somewhere around us, under us, above us, there is a sub natural world which we know nothing about, and these things, lets call them 'Subnatural Obsessionists For Energy', or S.N.O.F.E. For ease of understanding and clarity, spend all their time collecting this power and storing it, using it, where appropriate. They can't be seen directly, so they hide in the bottom of buckets, in worms holes in the garden, or amongst the grains of sand at the top of sandcastles. The innocent and unknowing donor receptors of bucket, lawn or sand are totally unaware of the violation of their souls, and without realising, help to generate ample stores for the S.N.O.F.E.s.

What I suggest, is that every time you see a windmill spinning, pull it out of the bucket, yank it out of the lawn, or tread on the sandcastle it's in. Hopefully these short circuits will disarm their power grid, convincing the S.N.O.F.E.s to share with us as humans, unknown secrets of natural power enhancement. It could be the start of global economy survival and environmental salvation. But keep it under your hat!.

Chapter Fourteen

The sky creates, or is it reflects, to some degree, our own present state of being.

Overcast and cold gives an air of doom and gloom, fast moving wind swept clouds and clean air make us feel alive and vibrant. Clear blue skies and powerful sun lend themselves to slow manual work or leisurely paced outdoor activities, whilst throw in a gentle breeze, and clam peace and tranquillity take over, especially if near water.

I was in a mood somewhere between clear blue skies, and clouds on the horizon.

I was happy enough and not particularly worried about anything, yet there was a distant feeling of caution and uncertainty, from what I didn't know precisely.

Then, as in a game of hide and seek, my body, through the tightening and clammy feel of my skin, the aches in my lower leg joints, and a degree of strain in my eyes causing a dull ache between them, jumped out and showed me the cause of my concern.

My mind and body were reminding me of my limits as far as staying in crowded areas was concerned. It usually manifests itself on bigger, more obvious visits to places such as London or Bristol, when you can smell and sense the dirty air at least thirty minutes before arriving there. You enjoy the sights, the sounds, even the smells, for a brief while, and then, after a period of time, with me usually a couple of days, you start yearning for fresh air to purge your lungs, for peace and quiet to calm your mind, and familiar things to welcome you home again, away from the impersonal, highly emotive and unresolving places.

So it was today, although in lesser league format. I found myself cursing the rumbling diesels of the buses, the snap happy attitude of the 'nip about town' cars, the pointless fashion of four wheel drive cars that women have adopted as their sociable mode of spewing out and vacuuming up of children from school, or negotiating the rigours of a supermarket car park.

Men use large and flash cars to improve (they think) their phallic prowess, so I can only assume women who drive these vehicles need to fulfil a similar insecurity.

My reaction is the same as that when I see promoted, American-style children's beauty pageants, where children are not the stars, merely the tools for creating a false sense of ability and purpose in the parents. I thought to myself, how sad.

I needed purging, a quick detox of these irritating social bugs, so I sought sanctuary, a place of anti-venom.

Luckily, off to my right was a sweet little bench surrounded by a Beech hedge and a manicured piece of lawn. With my back to the traffic, I could sit there searching up through the branches of the avenue of trees that shouldered up to this gentle little nook of paracetamol.

Quickly, I experienced my skeletal being relax, my skin settle, and my agitated state subside. Sat here back amongst a more suited environment, I felt like an old local sat in his favourite corner of a bar, where, amongst friends, he could join in with the sounds around him, or simply sit there, listening, reacting, enjoying.

After about five minutes, I felt calm and refreshed, so I bid my dues to the hedge and bench, acknowledged the stout trees, and returned to the busy pavement at roadside, ready, like a polished ornament, to receive my next covering of dust and fumes.

I didn't have to wait long before the sense of tarnishing took effect, as I walked back to the hive of activity that was amassed with people.

Trying to reason between why people act the way they do, and what makes them act the way they do I searched the surroundings for clues. My detective instinct was drawn to an alleyway, where, in between two buildings, tucked away and forgotten about, like some refugee, was a large and tattered looking piece of cardboard, the remains of a once neat and strong box.

Now in its abandoned state, it had assumed the sad role of social outcast, and this got me thinking.

Cardboard, on the whole gets a pretty rough deal. It has evolved from humble beginnings of mere reed parchments, has had to consistently seek, and fight for leadership status in the savage world of consumer packaging, where long and bloody battles have been fought with enemies such as polystyrene chips and sheets of bubble wrap. It has patiently waited while we as humans market test such products as vacuum-sealed packets and plastic containers. And now, when we have sensibly decided that the environmental benefits and the varied talents of cardboard should be encouraged, what do we humans do?, we go overboard.

We lap it up like some overweight nursery rhyme king, using as much as we can without thought to the effects, or systems on how to get rid of it, just as long as we fill the coffers.

Instead of thinking constructively on how we should make it, how it should be used in the most economically viable way, and above all how we could recycle the flattened boxes, carton inserts, and the protective coverings, thus reducing considerably the amount of shameful waste that we simply bury into the ground,

We blindly go on under filling boxes with ridiculously small objects, or stuffing them so full, the cardboard has no option but to submit to the bulk and split its sides open, treating our, what should be respected, Mr Cardboard like ugly cannon fodder. All this, in an attempt to satisfy the greedy and speed-driven monster that is today's retail market, where courier companies and distribution warehouses fight to be the fastest in the west, and where we, as lazy 'Old King Coles' are only interested in 'when and how much?', not 'as long as it arrives safely'.

Not enjoying the realisation that my mind was beginning to spin on the outer edges of a whirlpool of urban social studies, I quickly cut ties with thoughts on the subject.

I had raised the issue, now someone else could carry the plight of cardboard and fellow sufferers upon their shoulders.

Chapter Fifteen

Next to the alleyway a new shop front was being fitted, and what was once a shoe shop, (I knew this through the Hush Puppies posters still adorning the interior walls) was now being transformed into a gift shop, probably with items ranging from Buttercup paperweights, through scented candles, and on to tea towels and fudge.

As I looked across the street I felt the eyes of other established shop fronts, and imagined them whispering amongst themselves. "Have you seen what's moving in to No.78?" or "I say, there's a fine young filly of a gift shop" from the gent's outfitters; "So, you`re moving in here then are you?" from the dry cleaners, and, from the ladies' boutique, a touch of "We expect a certain standard along our High Street, I do hope you understand".

Like being in a school playground, or a pompous cheese and wine party our new gift shop front would need to get to know all the characters around her, know how to react when in conversation, yet maintain an individuality and a sense of identity. Shop front street credibility if you like. Maybe all towns have inanimate town committee made up of shop fronts, doorways, windows and buildings. In their fixed positions they hold monthly meetings and discuss subjects such as traffic flow, bicycle leaning, road sweeping regularity and extractor fan emissions.

This month's local bone of contention is the acceptable shades of colour for the paint currently being applied to the outside of our gift shop. Heated debates would rage over the benefits of ivory, the freshness of lemon sorbet, or the practicability of magnolia. Blues and, God forbid greens wouldn't get a look in.

Subconsciously, the acceptable colours would be transmitted to the mind of the decorating contractor who in turn would convince the owner.

It might also be that should an 'undesirable' move onto the high street, maybe a catalogue shop or a sex shop or a tattooist, then subtle innuendo and rumour would begin. Our self declared committee members having decided that it is their duty to 'encourage' the new import to move on, a slow and carefully planned programme of misinformation, undermining and 'unfortunate happenings' would prevail.

The test of character would end some weeks later with either the strength of the 'new boy' being respected and allowed to stay, or as in so many cases these days, the complete breakdown of its confidence and self belief. Windows would be whitewashed, doors locked, stock and fixtures removed until a mere empty shell is all that remains of a once proud and enthusiastic being.

Next time you pass a shop closing down, just pause and study the other shops around it. Is it lack of trade and profit that has caused this sad state, or is there something more sinister at work?

If there is, then communications would be vital to this unseen organisation. Telephone wires that we perceive as 'our' lines of communication are now more the nerve endings that pulsate information between our brick and block built Generals.

All feelings and information would be gathered and sent along these channels of data processing. At various strategic points along the high street 'spotters' such as lampposts or pillar boxes would keep tabs on the enemies goings-on. Camouflaged special unit drain covers and high surveillance specialists such as door handles and window boxes would all be orchestrated so that as much information as possible could be accumulated, before our residing Generals come to an evaluated conclusion. Long live the brave and free.

Down at my feet a piece of chewing gum, long since masticated, was doing its best impression of a pavement wart, or I suppose as it was at foot level we should give it the correct status of verruca. Weathered and hardened it had managed to maintain its off white colour but now had a toughened skin to it, in the style of a lung fish where, protected by its membrane it had gone into hibernation, waiting for the day the rains come, in the form of an industrial jet spray, when it can prise free again and revel in the torrents of water as it is washed across the now wet pavement river bed. Like the lung fish, not all rehatched specimens are as lucky and a large number get eaten by the next stage of the food chain, the council brush and shovel.

Fortunately, as so often in nature, enough specimens survive, supple and slimy, ready to either be remasticated, or used as a bonding agent between footwear and concrete, car tyre and tarmac. As this was still the 'dry' season, I left this particular lung fish in his hibernated state.

My nose must have been concentrating on other matters for it was now pointing me in the direction of a nearby public house. The unmistakable smell of stale beer with occasional mix of smoke and Prosan keg pipe cleaner did two things at the same time. It tempted you in for a quick pint or two, while reminding you of the result of going to excess.

Drinking, for me is like a New Year's resolution. You go out with all good intentions of an enjoyable evening, and yet, by a metaphorical April, say 10.15pm, you have thrown that idea out and are once again on the slippery slope to innards and brain awash with the alcoholic dehydrant and depressive nectar.

It was too bright a day to re-emerge into from such a dark place, and so walking passed its small bay windows I ogled the few mortals inside who were dry and in need of depressing.

Being a small town, I hadn't reached the irritability level of grime ridden state that I achieve when in large cities, yet bit by bit I could feel the place slowly casting a spell over me. I had had enough time here, here where I am only never more than sixty per cent comfortable and where I was always being reminded of the things I didn't like, and strove to keep away from.

I increased my pace to a 'Functional Strut' and, heading for the more open spaces at the end of the high street, began my escape route.

As I passed them, I could hear the shop fronts discussing

my case. Should they let me stay, should they help me on my way?

The gents outfitters were certainly on my side, as were the public house bay windows, the fruit and vegetable shop, the library and the ironmongers, but certainly I had bad vibes from the ladies hairdresser, the jewellers and the dry cleaners.

Eventually, reaching the last of the committee members, the ladies boutique, I afforded myself a half glance to my left towards its windows and I'm sure the full length curtains on either side closed slightly at the top, as if pushing eyebrows towards its nose, in some disapproval of my being there.

Guessing that its letterbox represented the pursed lips of this disgruntled member, I offered it, not a salute of respect, but blew it a kiss of total and utter defiance, little rascal that I am.

Chapter Sixteen

Walking into the more open market square I enjoyed the fact that the oppressive buildings on either side of the high street had now been replaced by more relaxed ones. These buildings didn't need the pretentiousness of the high street. They had sought, found and settled on their lot in life, happy to be a part of the local scene and know what part they played.

Directly in front of me was a delightful brick cottage which had merged with a catering business to become a charming set of tea rooms. No fancy frills, just simple, clean and elegant.

To its right, and my left, a previously arranged set of three terraced houses, which had been converted to a craft and design studio offering 'Daily tours' and 'individual' gift shop.

The other side of the tea rooms was given over to a small but neatly arranged car park capable of holding maybe twenty cars. What was nice here was that no ugly 'Pay Here' ticket machine kept reminding you of the cost of such comforts.

Instead, the attitude was first come first served, with no

time restriction. It never got overwhelmed and people generally were considerate on the matter of how long they had been parked there.

Being a non market day the square was empty apart from a couple of children sat bored on the war memorial, and the occasional delivery van outside one of the surrounding shops. I offered a silent 'alright lads' as I walked past but the expression on their faces showed no incentive to respond or indeed to do anything.

Passing along the side of the car park I took a path that led to a quiet tributary of the main river that ran around the town. Here in a small cove type backwater, a pair of rusting flood gates stood half submerged in the almost motionless water.

Long since the days of regular exercise, they had seized in this position and were now merely a stopping off point for broken strands of weed, various bits of reed and twigs and alas one or two empty beer cans.

All I needed was a ten foot long lever and a tub of industrial grease. I yearned to turn the massive cogs on top of the walkway and allow the gates one final and glorious dunking, thus allowing all debris to be washed away by the by the sudden current over them, then raise them clean and glistening, freshened and invigorated.

Pausing midway along the narrow concrete walkway that spanned the stream, I rested my forearms on the iron pole railing and looked gently into the clear water below. My sight searched through the miraged surface and on down to the muddy bottom some four or five feet under.

I allowed my mind, like the stream, to slowly amble along, gently picking up pieces of thought and carry them along for a while before allowing them their freedom.

No overhanging trees here, no swaying willows or rustling beeches, just open fields and meadow, cut like a through like a jigsaw by the curly bends of the river. The stream that I was suspended above would eventually rejoin its mother flow and take its journey to the next set of obstacles perhaps a mile or two downstream.

Protruding up through the edges of the narrow concrete slabs were the reinforcing rods. Their ends rounded and shiny from the hundreds of pairs of shoes which had stopped here, like me, to pause.

Fishing nets, jam jars and bait boxes would have all been placed here like a shrine to the religion of childhood pleasures. Anticipation and wonder mixed with a sense of risk and danger would serve to heighten the enjoyment.

I yearned to hold a rod in my hand now and experience the ecstatic shock of a bite, when all reactions trample over themselves in an attempt to deal with the situation. To realise and feel contact at the other end, to offer yourself to its challenge and to maintain calm exterior professionalism while inside, your stomach, head and heart are filled with adrenaline.

Your first sight of the new captive, a quick assessment of the difficulties, should you continue the fight? Of course you should, onwards then, maintaining the pressure, watching out for tricky manoeuvres, then finally, ah yes, the prey draws near. A quick flash of tail in a hopeless attempt to foil you before the damp net slides under its belly and then raises to encase it in the trap. No time for praise as both arms and hands work as a machine to retrieve both rod and net, working them in quickly to the safety of your sides, setting them down, separate from one another yet in unison.

Then and only then do you afford yourself the proud luxury of examining the catch. Instant respect for the noble creature oozes out of every pore as you tenderly take its net covering away, open its mouth and gently but firmly pull on the hook until it releases. There in front of you is your trophy, your reward, your result of battle.

To the victor the spoils, but now a decision. Do you keep it, offer it for the table, or do you show fortitude, and after a suitable moment of self admiration, return it warrior like, back to the aquatic land of its people.

As it gathers breath and with it strength, then slips silently away into its camouflaged world, a sense of dignity arises, swiftly followed by that sense of challenge, encouraging you to pit your wits once more.

Pushing up and off, away from the iron bar, I paused briefly for a final look, the doubled back towards the car park.

Instead of going back through the middle of the square, I turned right and walked passed the tea rooms and craft studio. Here a tiny alleyway squeezed me between two brick walls of above head height, until eventually I had no choice but to pop out back onto the high street.

Unlike Champagne, I had no cause to celebrate, for as I ventured to cross the first doorway, that of a children's clothing shop, a woman with a pushchair and no regard for the fact that because she was coming out of a shop and onto a busy thoroughfare, should maybe look first and give consideration to people already using the pavement, crashed straight into my right ankle.

Emphasising the crime with a slightly melodramatic

performance, I transmitted various telepathic messages to her in the hope of an apology. No chance. She simply tugged the pushchair back, causing the occupant to do an impression of a premier league header, and then pushed and turned said pushchair to join the masses in front of her. Without even a turn of the head for my well-being she left me, bending down rubbing my ankle and shin, looking like a disgruntled female Hollywood star, stretching and straightening her nylons in anticipation of a camera lens.

That did it. I needed to get out of there, get away from all that forged aggression, compression and irritation. The way people put up with intimate contact with people they don't know, don't want to know, yet keep coming back to all the trials and tribulations of, and all in the cause of, the sightseeing tour, the weekly shop, the visit to the bank, the hairdo, or simply the stepping stone whilst getting from A to B.

Limping slightly, though not as badly as a moment ago, I joined the opposing tides of people, walking like a crazed rugby player, offering a 'dummy' sideways move here, a 'halt and run' there, then seeing my a gap through the defence, made a dash for the try line where all action stopped and rest would be assured.

Not banking on a Jon Alloumou bus to my left, and a wiry Gareth Evans of an old lady pulling her shopping basket, who blanked me from centre right, I arrived victorious, battered and bruised over the kerb, placed the imaginary ball between the posts and left the conversion to one of my team mates.

Chapter Seventeen

I was being reminded of how badly fitting my shoes were, and now the constant nagging of my toes convinced me to allow them freedom from their present cocooned state.

Across the road the pavement gave way to a sandy drop-off where below, the welcoming sand beckoned. As I made the final skip and jump across the last slab of concrete I decided that my feet could wait a moment longer and I indulged myself the childhood pleasure of half jumping, half walking sideways down the side of the sandy slope. On arrival at the bottom of the fifteen foot dune I then shared my enjoyment with my feet.

Undoing my unsuitable shoes and then peeling off the grey cotton socks, I allowed a few moments to both allow my toes to wiggle ecstatically in the grains of sand, and to air the now empty shells of my leather uppers, before tying the laces together and placing the shoes around my neck to hang either side.

Immediately we all felt better. I felt better, my feet felt better, the world felt better, and as if on cue, the large cumulus clouds parted and allowed a surge of warm sunshine to pour down.

Instantly the shadows became sharper, colours intensified, and out across the sea, the waves sparkled like thousands of pieces of glass crystal.

Taking stock of my immediate surroundings, and agreeing with myself that the two other people on the beach were far away enough not to be considered a nuisance, I playfully marched towards the edge of the sand where the slow rising and falling sand-saturated surf pulled up the beach like a long tailed shirt in a washerwoman's strong hands, before recoiling back into the tub of soap suds, where time and time again it would be thrust up forward up the washboard beach.

Risking an unfavourable freak wave, I lay down along the tide mark and wriggled my elbows and hips until no uncomfortable lumps pressed into my bones. Turning my head seaward and laying it upon the semi-dry sand, I began watching the frothing lather float towards me on the ever shallowing water underneath.

There, in front of me, like a thousand Bumper cars jostling for space in a crowded arena were bubbles of all sizes, milling about in some crazed fever.

Eventually, as the force of their host transport system eased and then reversed, a sense of calm came over them as if they understood their place and accepted it, as if the ride had finished.

About eight inches in front of my face, a Limpet shell lay half buried, and with its proud apex showing I imagined it to be the fairground ride operator, calmly disregarding the mayhem and frantic activity going on around him, shouting to the other would be bubble riders waiting on the sides or at the top of the next wave, to "Roll Up, Roll Up" inviting them to "Come on now, Only fifty pence a ride".

Some would dawdle and think about it, some would avoid the ride totally, but some, especially those with younger, smaller offspring would hurry across the smoothed surface, trying to grab the nearest available ride before someone else.

It would be fun to watch the bubbles at night-time, with the stars above like brightly lit bulbs and the moonlight reflecting in their shiny spherical surfaces like the sparks that crackle when the Bumper cars' metal pole skims across the wire mesh ceiling. Regrettably, I could not wait for the evening performance for although I had all the time in the world, other things needed to be seen in daylight.

Rising, and brushing the sand from my clothes and from the side of my face, I quickly yet politely exchanged "Morning" with a lady who, walking her Red Setter dog had up until then thought me to be no more than a piece of railway sleeper, washed ashore after having been lost from some cargo vessel or dredger.

I saved her embarrassment, and mine, by not allowing the conversation to develop. Instead I began to walk away from her along the edge of the sand and continued a fair way before turning to confirm she had done the same. Alone again and next to the sea, I began to settle into my exploratory wanderings.

Walking along the beach, the fairground at my feet continued and, pleasant as it was, I moved inland ten feet to where the signs of last nights strong winds lay scattered randomly above the high water mark.

Pieces of sun dried seaweed, the odd plastic bottle top (why are they always blue?) A single flip flop, various bits of wood and a disposable lighter. All thrown together like the aftermath of a good party. All that was missing was the odd body part protruding from underneath, not obvious as to whether it was attached to anyone.

I supposed it's a double edged sword. Good that the rubbish isn't still floating around, polluting our seas, but the price we pay is having it on our beaches instead. Makes you wonder how much more is actually out there. Imagine a global desk sergeant somewhere in an environmental charge room, handing back our belongings as we take account of our crime; "Now then sir, seven thousand pocket lighters, four hundred and sixty four various items of footwear, eight hundred and eighty one oil drums - empty, four thousand shampoo bottles - various makes", etc etc, you get the picture. Like most crimes, it's easy to give theoretical solutions to their prevention, but seven times out of ten we need to look a little closer to home. I stop there, for I feel there is enough spent driftwood along our shores, without me adding another soapbox to the pile.

Now in the middle of the beach my pace was checked by the softer sand, allowing my feet to sink in each time and allow my toes the pleasure of an exfoliating massage.

My head, now in Radar mode, was scanning the vista before me from left to right through one hundred and eighty degrees, quickly noting any points of interest. The tanker out at sea sat on the horizon to my right, the wave topped tide sweeping down channel, now halfway through its second ebb of the day. The wooden groins pointing out to sea, one behind the other, each like a lifeguard, responsible for its own piece of beach. The cliff top where the strong tufts of grass would be swaying in defiance to the strength and direction of the sea breeze, now at its height. Behind the cliffs a landscape of fields, hedgerows and trees, unique to this land, where rich watery greens and vibrant blue skies with their crisp white clouds, embellish the good things of the countryside.

By a sheer fluke, I trod on a sharp piece of shell which brought me to a sudden halt. Looking down, I realised my good fortune by the fact I had avoided, but only just, pressing an imprint of a steel bolt head into my kneecap. The wooden groin was suddenly laid before me and it now took my full attention. I crouched down and studied its sun drenched side. Soft vivid green seaweed adorned the parts still reached by the sea. It looked like the wood had sprouted fur and, gently running my hand down its surface, the texture was that of a cuddly teddy bear, soft, smooth and comforting.

At its base, a small channel, perhaps two inches wide had been carved out in the sand by the receding waves as they had run along its barrier. Here the top sand had been flushed away to reveal the nugget-like pebbles underneath.

Closer to the sea, larger clumps of seaweed had anchored themselves to the solid planks and were enjoying a siesta before the return of their watery surroundings.

Hanging limp, in the warm sunshine, I left them to snooze and moved back up along the groin to the drier parts where only sun and wind held any threat to their existence. Here, the sun bleached wood gave off a stone-like appearance, with only the visible grain betraying the illusion.

Here I sat for a while, enjoying the warm sun on my face and neck, with the gentle meandering breeze rocking me slowly from side to side. My stretched out legs felt heavy against the sand and sleep would have been a very nearby destination had it not been for the fact I could not settle my hands. I rested them behind my head. No good. Laid them crossed on my thighs but they inclined to rise to my chest where folding and unfolding arms heightened the state of activity. Finally I had to restrain them and this I did by placing face down on the sand and sliding them under each leg where a final wriggle of the hips secured them fast.

I had a good ten minutes before the lady and her dog, who had now turned again, would be able to see the whites of my eyes, and thus enjoying my solitude, gently closed my eyes and let the music of the sea slop around in my head. There would be slow quiet pieces, then, building to a finish, I would listen and wait for the waves to curl along their edge, like some 1920's lady dance troop, before crashing down and spilling themselves across the sand.

Eventually, the far away barking came closer and closer, and opening one eye, established contact with the Red Setter who, half out of playfulness and half out of uncertain curiosity, was assessing this new possible playmate. If I didn't want to talk to the lady earlier on, I certainly wasn't going to open a debate with her better half. Instead, I closed my open eye again and, gambling on him getting bored, said nothing and sat quite still.

A few requests from his owner eventually took him away from me. The lady was probably delightful to talk to and I might have spent a thoroughly enjoyable ten minutes larking around with the dog, but for now, as for most of the time, I didn't feel like making an effort, just to be polite. Alone again with the sea symphony and acoustics of wind

I took myself to that half sleeping state you go too. Not allowing myself to sink into total sleep, just listening on the surface. This would be a very pleasant half hour.

Twelve minutes later I needed something to do, so rising stiffly with that metallic taste in my mouth, and stretching what I could from my back and shoulders I picked up my shoes and, stepping over the low part of the groin, continued on up the beach.

Licking my lips I discovered salt, which was both nice and annoying. Nice because the sea had made spoken to me but annoying because it reminded me I was thirsty. Squeezing saliva from the inside of my cheeks I created enough to swallow a couple of times and this helped to satisfy my thirst, at least temporarily.

The ground on my left gave way to a steadily rising bank of sand dunes. All along their length were pathways, cut through them by eager children, enthusiastic with the excitement of a day on the beach. Growing randomly around these paths were the wonderful clumps of long bladed dune grass, adding interest to an otherwise blank canvas of sand.

At different levels and forming cosy little pockets of shelter from the stiff sea breezes these grass walls prove most useful to courting couples who are in need of some privacy, or, the good old British tourist who, no matter how cold, how windy or how cloudy it may be, he has come to the seaside, and see the seaside he will. Here in these little cubicles he can stake his claim and set out his windbreak, his folding chair, flask, blanket and binoculars. 'Dug in' for the day like some holiday making mercenary.

I love the feel of these grasses, the sense of security they offer as you lay your head back amongst them. One needs an ability to ignore the sand in the ears and the constant flickering of sand flies that seem to hop rather than fly around the base of the clumps. This ability achieved, no finer place can be found in which to absorb the whole ensemble of sky, sea, land, sun and air.

It was whilst laying back in one of these clumps, with just knees, lower legs and feet showing out the side, that I went into my examination mode. That mode where you drift from real time and fact, and really study hard the detail immediately in front of you.

Suddenly, like watching the glowing embers of a fire, you stare really hard at a patch, about one foot square, and become transfixed by the detail therein. You become aware of what is actually in there, has been all the time but has been hidden by our real time actions. Now in the 'Detail World', small stones, tiny flecks of shell, basal roots of plants, anything within your patch of study draws all your energy, your concentration, and focuses your imagination on their world of existence, shows their place in the context of things.

A ripple in the sand, a Roman fortress, a curly root sticking out, a water park slide, a half domed shell, a Chinese hat or a beautifully carved shallow wooden bowl. Sometimes nothing, just the art of staring and seeing nothing at all, but still staring.

Chapter Eighteen

The tennis ball hitting my nose was probably the cause of my concentration break rather than a stupid Red Setters expression, looking down at me with rear end swaying as it threw the tail from side to side.

Not angry as I thought I might be, but more in a 'Now that's not very clever is it' expression and body language, I passed the ball to the awaiting mouth, and on acceptance, suggested to him to go away and not come back. Amazingly he seemed to understand the first part, but failed miserably on the second, for a matter of ten seconds later the familiar heavy breathing and psychopathic wining had returned.

By gesturing to the lady, by way of airport ground crew manoeuvres and hand signalling accompanied by a fixed beauty contest smile, I managed, I hope, to convey that her 'wonderful, obedient, likeable and oh yes playful isn't he' friend, was once again invading my space.

Unlike me, with a simple whistle and hand slap on the thigh the owner convinced the beast to return. Thinking with the philosophy of 'third time lucky', I hoped that would be the last encounter with the six legged party of two.

Time to seek new places now, and so along the winding pathway and up around the seaward face of the cliff. At the top I turned and faced the sea, receiving the full effect of vista and sea breeze.

I love the way the air completely washes through you. It throws up your hair and swirls it around like a tornado picking up branches. The air rushes in and up your nostrils then dives deep into your lungs where it immediately kicks out any stale carbon dioxide. Your face becomes alive as its skin absorbs the cleansing blast and your half closed eyes water as they try to remain moist, and keep the intense glare off the sea to a minimum. I sucked in volumes of this invigorating life force and felt my whole body revel in its magical power.

Turning away from the source and facing inland, it was as if someone had suddenly switched off the fans and turned the volume down. In complete contrast the stillness, the grey muted colours of the path and the shadows behind me made me feel alone, vulnerable, chilled. There was not enough there to convince me to stay and so, facing once more to seaward, I began strolling across the top of the cliff towards its end, about half a mile away.

At my feet and all around me, great swards of swaying chameleon-like grasses curled to and fro, going from left to right, going from light to dark as they caused their own shadows. Every thirty yards or so I would stoop down and brush my hand over the swirling masses, sensing their texture and resilience.

Twenty minutes or so later I found myself at the end, and edge, of this particular headland and took advantage of a wooden seat which had been strategically placed, in memory of a loved one. Kicking out each leg straight I leant back against the wooden struts and gave a relaxing sigh.

Looking out across the wide gently swelling bay below me, my eyes took me far out to sea as if on some visual expedition. Up here, my horizon was much further than the one the six legged party of two would be looking at down on the beach.

Was this reflective, I pondered, of how we each saw our existence, and if this was indicative of our own goals and aspirations. I know it was certainly true in my case. For many years now, exploration, travel, experimentation, curiosity have all played a vital role in my existence. Okay, I'm the first to admit I enjoy the basic home comforts, but it is a never diminishing quest for information and awareness that is the backbone of my character.

Maybe our six legged party of two shared such a mental makeup, and maybe I was totally wide of the mark. I had no intention of solving that particular puzzle.

Instead, I selfishly assumed that their world began at 8.00am with cornflakes and coffee, and ended at 10.00pm with late film and biscuits. At least this way my theory of horizons would stand up in my own psychological courtroom.

I felt someone was watching me. That certain feeling of vulnerability and clumsiness wafted over me. Not wanting to appear shocked or surprised, I fumbled in an attempt to look natural, and turned round to my left, aiming my vision, not directly at my stalker, but guessing at an area just out of direct eye contact.

Foolishness and anger quickly followed, as there, sat on a

fence post, looking all full of himself, was a blessed seagull. Acting smug and as 'jobsworth' as you can get, he occasionally adjusted his stance with either a sideways step where one foot was raised and then purposefully lowered, or a quick quiver of his tail feathers. Unsure of his thoughts and intentions, owing to a fixed expression on his face, I took the incentive, and shouted him off his perch.

Seagulls, the laughing hyenas of the coastal resort, sniggering at the mannerisms of the tourists, blatant screaming in disregard of ones peace and solitude.

We have been raised to accept the screeching cawing of the seagull, made to believe it is part of the tapestry of seaside living or nautical fulfilment, or, like postcards, a necessity to tourists.

Well, no more. I hereby swing a hammer at the mould of pretence and smash its sides open. I look upon these loud brackish creatures as one does a loud mouthed bully. A lost soul, a sad example of misplaced energy, a need to be heard.

If instead of peer pressure, gang survival and street credibility, these souls were listened to, spoke to at their level, given the opportunity to fail as much as to succeed, and directed where needed, a bond, a trust, a respect, a pride would be born where the individual could shine and sing out on his/her own terms. Creating, performing, living. Instead, the seagull now seems not only set on a course of public displeasure, but is now, at the second stage, where the sense of hating what one does has past, and now needs to create a fuss merely to be noticed.

If only the ornithological brotherhood of evolved species

(O.B.O.E.S) could see what is happening, then maybe a 'halfway house' system, or a counselling clinic, for such unfortunate souls could be set up and managed.

Eagles and Kingfishers, Owls and Swans could offer funded tutorials and workshops on their successes. Other similar fated, or more hardened and experienced characters who have been through the wringer could offer warnings and advice. Crows and Starlings could warn of being seen as gothic and dark icons, and Sparrows and House martins could offer streetwise sensibility.

All these things could surely help the plight of our poor old Seagull who is, I think, still worth fighting for.

Imagine, no more 'Go on, get out of it!' or 'Ah no, look what that thing's just done!'. Instead, as one approached the coast, smelt the air, and felt sand between toes, you could simply gaze upwards at the circling, swooping creatures, now possessing style and confidence but without their attitude of vengeance, and merely offer 'Hey dude, winds light and warm on the updrafts man!', before drifting off into a more relaxed immersion in your surroundings.

Chapter Nineteen

Having satisfied my curiosity that yes, the top of the cliff was still there, I took a cross path that led to the main track leading back down to the beach.

Gazing out across the sea again, grey clouds had started to lay claim to the lower sky and the gentle white clouds above my head had heeded their warning and were beginning to pick up their pace.

Now bathed in the remainder of the sunshine, with the grey masses as a backdrop, the headland on the western side of the bay seemed to stretch itself out along the horizon like some geological crocodile, waking up from its 'warm up' session. Now ready for a meal it had started to swagger out into the open sea where, just breaking the surface, it would glide up to its prey, maybe a tanker or cruise ship, and without warning, engulf them with a single tremendous snap of its jaw.

Then it would take them down to the deeper water and begin the merciless 'death roll' of its victims. Now demised and helpless, the vessels would be released to slowly drift down and sink to the sand and shingle bottom of the crocodiles ocean larder. Here, they would 'ripen' and mature until their flesh and taste would suit our captors palate.

After a gorging meal, the bones would be left to rot down and become part of the next millennium's sedimentary rock strata.

Perhaps most shipwrecks aren't due to navigational error or severe weather. I thought of all the people who day sail past these grey/green rocky headlands and wondered if they ever really study the boulders, the scoring on the rock face and the apparently stationery top edge of the cliffs.

I myself had been on this particular 'croc' too long, and just in case it was in a 'sly fox and gingerbread man' frame of mind, I excused myself slightly faster than I had welcomed him.

Feeling safer now away from the ominously sleek creature I walked back down to the tarmac road once more. Although a road by practical means, it seldom saw traffic. The odd lost tourist or a pair of cyclists, but not much more. With the verges doing their best to encroach over the edges, its sides were mainly tall grasses occasionally contrasted with a sprawling green leafed plant.

On my left was the wide open sea with all its history, vivid dreams, changing moods and international accolades. To my right, the unknown quieter character. That of the small more sheltered inlet of water where river met sea in a foyer of a tidal bowl, which twice a day would fill and twice a day empty. Now at almost high tide and filling to the brim, the breeze was opposing the direction of the flow causing regular wavelets to build up. Its surface no longer invited setting suns or the photographers' lens but instead the admiration of a couple of hikers out on a brisk walk.

This was its chance to perform and dance to its audience, unlike winter when it had to follow a more regimented routine. Now it could cause sparkles of light to hop and skip, lavish itself with decorations of seaweed and driftwood, entice things to get up and take part in its street market performance.

Slowly these unwilling volunteers took their place in the show. Whippy young trees would indicate the next movement and move to the score. Like a chorus line of ballet shoes running up to front of stage, the tiny surf would rush up then stop at the tide mark where it would dissipate over the slimy green pebbles.

Boats, like tethered cattle accepted the plot, their bows rising and falling as they chewed on the ripples beneath them. Some with matted coats, looking drawn and shabby while some have the appearance of a well groomed and glossy more athletic shape of a racing breed. Most Sundays, tide permitting, their owners release them from their leashes and allow them the freedom of running around the open bay, pulling on their tillers and sails as if reins. After a good thrash about they are guided back, with varying amounts of skill, as some buck or walk backwards, to their grazing grounds. Here they are rubbed down, cleaned, tidied and some covered with a blanket before their owners or jockeys give them a couple of friendly taps on their flanks, or even a kiss, and leave their trusted steeds contentedly bobbing away until next time.

Some models get taken out two or three times a week, for these are the thoroughbreds of the racing circuits. Their owners obliged to regularly test their boats, and themselves, against the combination of tide and wind, and that other far more complicated system of highs and lows, calms and storms, namely fellow competitors. All chasing an invisible target, week in, week out trying to accumulate points in an effort to 'outdo' each other and be the year's top gun.

Lapwings waddle along the wet shore like a group of demented trainee traffic wardens. Hands behind their backs, checking things here, then back over there. Another quick scurry to check that this pebble or this piece of seaweed is entitled to park there. Occasionally the sea speaks for all of us and chases them up the beach causing a look of "No need to be like that is their sir" from our uniformed officials. Their course instructor shows them how to hold their hands correctly behind their backs and stroll in that annoying manner. The less confident ones at the back trying to keep up on all levels while the confident students all huddle at the front trying to impress their mentor. He shows them how to approach a possible `target`. The quick double waddle and stop manoeuvre, or the casual look at the ground and scuff your feet before raising your eyes routine. All day they are drilled and instructed, pacing this way and that, so that one day when movements have been finely honed, they can be released into the coastal and estuary environments where they can spend their time annoying everyone around them.

At the seaward end of one of the groins stood a lone figure of a fisherman. As if at the end of the world, he cast his weight and baited hook as far as he could, in the hope of making contact with something, anything. Surrounded by a cluster of large reinforcing rocks, and stood under the red can on top of the rusty pole, the whole scene reminded me of a reject art-deco table lamp, its colourful top above a dull cast metal base. I imagined a shoal of rock wrasse swimming around the rocks below the fisherman's feet, in gang formation and in full knowledge of his plight. Indeed, these were hardened and sly rock wrasse who enjoyed challenging anyone silly enough to attempt their capture. Picking at bits of ragworm from our anglers hook, they would occasionally tease him by jerking the line, either by a quick grab at the weight with their mouths, or a quick flash of rear tail at a point above the weight. This would serve two purposes. Firstly it would encourage our long suffering and ever hopeful friend to stay and continue his quest, and secondly, ensure the hook, once hauled in and checked, would be thrown back in topped up with a new juicy ragworm. As if in a reverse scene of Upstairs Downstairs, our wrasse would summon their butler to satisfy some whimsical game.

Finally, after about five or six hours of this cordial vertical ping pong our stalwart angler would reel in, pack his kit together and head off home, putting the disappointing outcome of his efforts down to the 'luck and enjoyment of the sport', innocently unaware of our gang of fish chortling away and blowing defiant bubbles behind his back.

Chapter Twenty

The sensors on my body were foretelling of a change in the weather, as the atmospheric pressure seemed to be rising. The sky overhead at present was stirring from its siesta and was showing signs of going back to work. Behind me I noticed a rainbow erupting from someone's roof and arching over until it disappeared into a copse of trees.

Maybe rainbows aren't semicircular apparitions at all, but are always complete circles, whereby there is always a hidden portion of them deep in the ground that no one 'up top' ever sees. If we assume a Ying Yang theory and we only see the fresh clean and pure colours above the ground in the sky, then maybe as it goes underground, the colours drop their 'Julie Andrews' characteristics and become these hideous, violent and retched creatures. All fighting one another and creating a world of deceit and filth.

During the next part of the curve they begin to wonder if this really is the life for them, or if indeed they prefer the life 'above'. Greens that were once vibrant and lush have now become slimy and muddied. Yellows alive with warmth and clarity now appear as custard on a dull day.

Reds simply give up the fight and become slaves to the destiny of others, and as for once enchanting blues, a fast downward spiral has taken them from self confidence and status to a sad lonely state of insecurity and betrayal.

They now make a choice, and seek counselling and a halfway house, just below the surface, where any tarnishes and any feelings of self doubt are removed. Then, and only then, do they rise merrily up into the open sky, rejoicing in their new freedom, shining and dancing in the atmosphere, reformed characters.

A glance at my wrist told me two things. My arm seemed to be getting more freckles, and secondly, it was 5.23pm. Either that or it was now 6.00pm and I needed new batteries.

It was now that time of day, the interim between afternoon play and evening events. The time for ending one part of the day before beginning the next, a time to return somewhere before setting out somewhere else. Cars would be packed up with families, bicycles, bats and balls, rods, rubber rings and li-los. Trains would be packed with commuters, shops would be re-packed with stock and in homes, ovens packed with dinners.

None of the above appealed to me and I decided to try my hand at a variant of time travel whereby I stand still and time passes me by. I would remain here through the days interim and then move on. Would I be molecularly modified or sprout mutations of myself as this warp in time took place. It was a risk, but like all great explorers and scientists - Shackleton, Einstein, I faced my critics and prepared myself.

The actual art of sitting down in a four-way cliff top shelter isn't that hard, and even crossing ones legs whilst deciding if the lump of white on the ground in front of you is old chewing gum or solidified paint doesn't pose too much of a challenge. What did surprise me, mainly because of my inexperience of such things, was how uncomfortable four strips of wood, making themselves out to be a bench, could be. I had expected, as with all things scientific experimentation, a degree of uncertainty and anomaly, causing some discomfort and irritation, but this was buttock numbing and chafe irritably awful. No wonder poodles look so miserable when made to sit up next to their more suited round bottomed owners.

After half an hour I could take no more and decided to pull the plug on interfering with time.

So it was that at 5.53pm, or in the case of new batteries, 6.30pm I took myself off on a new venture. A quest to find the next interesting and maybe familiar place.

Simon R. Brickell
20 Hobart Road
New Milton
Hants
BH25 6EG
England
UK
Tel 01425 616294